I RATHER WITH THE LEAPING TROUT
WIND AMONG LILIES IN AND OUT.

UNDERWOODS

Of all my verse, like not a single line ;
But like my title, for it is not mine.
That title from a better man I stole :
Ah, how much better, had I stol'n the whole !

A CHILD'S GARDEN OF VERSES

BY

ROBERT LOUIS STEVENSON

Volume Fifteen

NEW YORK
PETER FENELON COLLIER, PUBLISHER

CONTENTS

VOLUME FIFTEEN

UNDERWOODS

BOOK I.—IN ENGLISH

CHAPTER		PAGE
I.	Envoy	17
II.	A Song of the Road	17
III.	The Canoe Speaks	19
IV.	It is the Season	20
V.	The House Beautiful	22
VI.	A Visit from the Sea	23
VII.	To a Gardener	24
VIII.	To Minnie	26
IX.	To K. de M.	26
X.	To N. V. de G. S.	27
XI.	To Will. H. Low	29
XII.	To Mrs. Will. H. Low	30
XIII.	To H. F. Brown	31
XIV.	To Andrew Lang	33
XV.	Et tu in Arcadia vixisti	34
XVI.	To W. E. Henley	37
XVII.	Henry James	39
XVIII.	The Mirror Speaks	39
XIX.	Katharine	41
XX.	To F. J. S.	41
XXI.	Requiem	42
XXII.	The Celestial Surgeon	42
XXIII.	Our Lady of the Snows	43
XXIV.	Not yet, my soul	46

CONTENTS

CHAPTER   PAGE

XXV. It is not yours, O mother, to complain............ 48

XXVI. The Sick Child.. 50

XXVII. In Memoriam F. A. S............................... 51

XXVIII. To my Father.. 52

XXIX. In the States.. 54

XXX. A Portrait.. 54

XXXI. Sing clearlier, Muse................................ 55

XXXII. A Camp... 56

XXXIII. The Country of the Camisards.................. 56

XXXIV. Skerryvore 57

XXXV. Skerryvore: The Parallel......................... 57

XXXVI. My house, I say..................................... 58

XXXVII. My body which my dungeon is.................. 58

XXXVIII. Say not of me that weakly I declined............. 60

BOOK II.—IN SCOTS

I. The Maker to Posterity....................................... 62

II. Ille Terrarum... 64

III. When aince Aprile has fairly come.................... 67

IV. A Mile an' a Bittock................................... 68

V. A Lowden Sabbath Morn.............................. 69

VI. The Spaewife... 76

VII. The Blast—1875.. 77

VIII. The Counterblast—1886............................... 79

IX. The Counterblast Ironical............................ 82

X. Their Laureate to an Academy Class Dinner Club...... 83

XI. Embro Hie Kirk... 86

XII. The Scotsman's Return from Abroad................. 89

XIII. Late in the Nicht...................................... 93

XIV. My Conscience.. 96

XV. To Doctor John Brown................................. 98

XVI. It's an owercome sooth for age an' youth............. 101

A CHILD'S GARDEN OF VERSES

CHAPTER   PAGE

I. Bed in Summer 107

II. A Thought 107

III. At the Seaside 108

IV. Young Night Thought 108

V. Whole Duty of Children 109

VI. Rain 109

VII. Pirate Story 110

VIII. Foreign Lands 111

IX. Windy Nights 112

X. Travel 112

XI. Singing 114

XII. Looking Forward 115

XIII. A Good Play 115

XIV. Where go the Boats? 116

XV. Auntie's Skirts 117

XVI. The Land of Counterpane 117

XVII. The Land of Nod 118

XVIII. My Shadow 119

XIX. System 120

XX. A Good Boy 121

XXI. Escape at Bedtime 122

XXII. Marching Song 123

XXIII. The Cow 124

XXIV. Happy Thought 124

XXV. The Wind 125

XXVI. Keepsake Mill 126

XXVII. Good and Bad Children 127

XXVIII. Foreign Children 128

XXIX. The Sun's Travels 129

XXX. The Lamplighter 130

XXXI. My Bed is a Boat 131

XXXII. The Moon 132

XXXIII. The Swing 132

XXXIV. Time to Rise 133

XXXV. Looking-Glass River 133

CHAPTER		PAGE
XXXVI.	Fairy Bread	135
XXXVII.	From a Railway Carriage	135
XXXVIII.	Winter-Time	136
XXXIX.	The Hayloft	137
XL.	Farewell to the Farm	138
XLI.	Northwest Passage:	
	1. Good-Night	139
	2. Shadow March	140
	3. In Port	140

THE CHILD ALONE

I.	The Unseen Playmate	142
II.	My Ship and I	143
III.	My Kingdom	144
IV.	Picture-Books in Winter	146
V.	My Treasures	147
VI.	Block City	148
VII.	The Land of Story-Books	149
VIII.	Armies in the Fire	150
IX.	The Little Land	151

GARDEN DAYS

I.	Night and Day	155
II.	Nest Eggs	157
III.	The Flowers	158
IV.	Summer Sun	159
V.	The Dumb Soldier	160
VI.	Autumn Fires	162
VII.	The Gardener	163
VIII.	Historical Associations	164

ENVOYS

I.	To Willie and Henrietta	166
II.	To my Mother	167
III.	To Auntie	167
IV.	To Minnie	167
V.	To my Name-Child	170
VI.	To any Reader	172

UNDERWOODS

DEDICATION

———

THERE are men and classes of men that stand above the common herd: the soldier, the sailor, and the shepherd not infrequently; the artist rarely; rarelier still, the clergyman; the physician almost as a rule. He is the flower (such as it is) of our civilization; and when that stage of man is done with, and only remembered to be marveled at in history, he will be thought to have shared as little as any in the defects of the period, and most notably exhibited the virtues of the race. Generosity he has, such as is possible to those who practice an art, never to those who drive a trade; discretion, tested by a hundred secrets; tact, tried in a thousand embarrassments; and what are more important, Heraclean cheerfulness and courage. So it is that he brings air and cheer into the sickroom, and often enough, though not so often as he wishes, brings healing.

Gratitude is but a lame sentiment; thanks,

(9)

when they are expressed, are often more embar-
rassing than welcome; and yet I must set forth
mine to a few out of many doctors who have
brought me comfort and help: to Dr. Willey of
San Francisco, whose kindness to a stranger it
must be as grateful to him, as it is touching to
me, to remember; to Dr. Karl Ruedi of Davos, the
good genius of the English in his frosty mountains; to Dr. Herbert of Paris, whom I knew
only for a week, and to Dr. Caissot of Mont-
pellier, whom I knew only for ten days, and who
have yet written their names deeply in my
memory; to Dr. Brandt of Royat; to Dr. Wake-
field of Nice; to Dr. Chepmell, whose visits
make it a pleasure to be ill; to Dr. Horace
Dobell, so wise in counsel; to Sir Andrew Clark,
so unwearied in kindness; and to that wise
youth, my uncle, Dr. Balfour.

I forget as many as I remember; and I ask
both to pardon me, these for silence, those for
inadequate speech. But one name I have kept
on purpose to the last, because it is a household
word with me, and because if I had not received
favors from so many hands and in so many
quarters of the world, it should have stood upon
this page alone: that of my friend Thomas Bod-
ley Scott of Bournemouth. Will he accept this,
although shared among so many, for a dedication

to himself? and when next my ill-fortune (which has thus its pleasant side) brings him hurrying to me when he would fain sit down to meat or lie down to rest, will he care to remember that he takes this trouble for one who is not fool enough to be ungrateful?

R. L. S.

SKERRYVORE,
BOURNEMOUTH.

NOTE

THE human conscience has fled of late the troublesome domain of conduct for what I should have supposed to be the less congenial field of art: there she may now be said to rage, and with special severity in all that touches dialect; so that in every novel the letters of the alphabet are tortured, and the reader wearied, to commemorate shades of mispronunciation. Now, spelling is an art of great difficulty in my eyes, and I am inclined to lean upon the printer, even in common practice, rather than to venture abroad upon new quests. And the Scots tongue has an orthography of its own, lacking neither "authority nor author." Yet the temptation is great to lend a little guidance to the bewildered Englishman. Some simple phonetic artifice might defend your verses from barbarous mishandling, and yet not injure any vested interest. So it seems at first; but there are rocks ahead. Thus, if I wish the diphthong *ou* to have its proper value, I may write *oor* instead of *our;* many have done so and lived, and the pillars of the universe remained unshaken. But if I did so, and came presently to *doun*, which is the classical Scots spelling of the English *down*, I should begin to feel uneasy; and if I went on a little further, and came to a classical Scots word, like *stour* or *dour* or *clour*, I should know precisely where I was—that is to say, that I was out of sight of land on those high seas of spelling reform in which so many strong swimmers have toiled vainly. To some the situation is exhilarating; as for me, I give one bubbling cry and sink. The compromise at which I have arrived is indefensible, and I have no thought of trying to defend it. As I have stuck for the most part to the proper spelling, I append a table of some common vowel sounds which no one need consult; and just to prove that I belong to my age and have in me the stuff of a reformer, I have used modification marks throughout. Thus I can tell myself, not without pride, that I have added a fresh stumbling-block for English readers, and to a page of print in my native tongue have lent a new uncouthness. *Sed non nobis.*

I note again, that among our new dialecticians, the local habitat of every dialect is given to the square mile. I could not emulate this nicety if I desired; for I simply wrote my Scots as well as I was able, not caring if it hailed from Lauderdale or Angus, from the Mearns or Galloway; if I had ever heard a good word, I used it without shame; and when Scots was lacking, or the rhyme jibbed, I was glad (like my betters) to fall back on English. For all that, I own to a friendly feeling for the tongue of Fergusson and of Sir Walter, both Edinburgh men; and I confess that Burns has always sounded in my ear like something partly foreign. And indeed I am from the Lothians myself; it is there I heard the language spoken about my childhood; and it is in the drawling Lothian voice that I repeat it to myself. Let the precisians call my speech that of the Lothians. And if it be not pure, alas! what matters it? The day draws near when this illustrious and malleable tongue shall be quite forgotten; and Burns's Ayrshire, and Dr. Macdonald's Aberdeen-awa', and Scott's brave, metropolitan utterance will be all equally the ghosts of speech. Till then I would love to have my hour as a native Maker, and be read by my own countryfolk in our own dying language: an ambition surely rather of the heart than of the head, so restricted as it is in prospect of endurance, so parochial in bounds of space.

BOOK I — IN ENGLISH

I

ENVOY

Go, little book, and wish to all
Flowers in the garden, meat in the hall,
A bin of wine, a spice of wit,
A house with lawns inclosing it,
A living river by the door,
A nightingale in the sycamore!

II

A SONG OF THE ROAD

THE gauger walked with willing foot,
And aye the gauger played the flute;
And what should Master Gauger play
But *Over the hills and far away?*

Whene'er I buckle on my pack
And foot it gayly in the track,
O pleasant gauger, long since dead,
I hear you fluting on ahead.

You go with me the self-same way—
The self-same air for me you play;
For I do think and so do you
It is the tune to travel to.

For who would gravely set his face
To go to this or t'other place?
There's nothing under heav'n so blue
That's fairly worth the traveling to.

On every hand the roads begin,
And people walk with zeal therein;
But wheresoe'er the highways tend,
Be sure there's nothing at the end.

Then follow you, wherever hie
The traveling mountains of the sky.
Or let the streams in civil mode
Direct your choice upon a road;

For one and all, or high or low,
Will lead you where you wish to go;
And one and all go night and day
Over the hills and far away!

Forest of Montargis, 1878.

III

THE CANOE SPEAKS

On the great streams the ships may go
About men's business to and fro.
But I, the egg-shell pinnace, sleep
On crystal waters ankle-deep:
I, whose diminutive design,
Of sweeter cedar, pithier pine,
Is fashioned on so frail a mold,
A hand may launch, a hand withhold:
I, rather, with the leaping trout
Wind, among lilies, in and out;
I, the unnamed, inviolate,
Green, rustic rivers navigate;
My dipping paddle scarcely shakes
The berry in the bramble-brakes;
Still forth on my green way I wend
Beside the cottage garden-end;
And by the nested angler fare,
And take the lovers unaware.
By willow wood and water-wheel
Speedily fleets my touching keel;
By all retired and shady spots
Where prosper dim forget-me-nots;
By meadows where at afternoon
The growing maidens troop in June

To loose their girdles on the grass.
Ah! speedier than before the glass
The backward toilet goes; and swift
As swallows quiver, robe and shift
And the rough country stockings lie
Around each young divinity.
When, following the recondite brook,
Sudden upon this scene I look,
And light with unfamiliar face
On chaste Diana's bathing-place,
Loud ring the hills about and all
The shallows are abandoned. . . .

———

IV

It is the season now to go
About the country high and low,
Among the lilacs hand in hand,
And two by two in fairy land.

The brooding boy, the sighing maid,
Wholly fain and half afraid,
Now meet along the hazel'd brook
To pass and linger, pause and look.

A year ago, and blithely paired,
Their rough-and-tumble play they shared;

They kissed and quarreled, laughed and
    cried,
A year ago at Eastertide.

With bursting heart, with fiery face,
She strove against him in the race;
He, unabashed, her garter saw,
That now would touch her skirts with
    awe.

Now by the stile ablaze she stops,
And his demurer eyes he drops;
Now they exchange averted sighs
Or stand and marry silent eyes.

And he to her a hero is,
And sweeter she than primroses;
Their common silence dearer far
Than nightingale and mavis are.

Now when they sever wedded hands,
Joy trembles in their bosom-strands,
And lovely laughter leaps and falls
Upon their lips in madrigals.

———

V

THE HOUSE BEAUTIFUL

A naked house, a naked moor,
A shivering pool before the door,
A garden bare of flowers and fruit,
And poplars at the garden foot:
Such is the place that I live in,
Bleak without and bare within.

Yet shall your ragged moor receive
The incomparable pomp of eve,
And the cold glories of the dawn
Behind your shivering trees be drawn;
And when the wind from place to place
Doth the unmoored cloud-galleons chase,
Your garden gloom and gleam again,
With leaping sun, with glancing rain.
Here shall the wizard moon ascend
The heavens, in the crimson end
Of day's declining splendor; here
The army of the stars appear.
The neighbor hollows dry or wet,
Spring shall with tender flowers beset;
And oft the morning muser see
Larks rising from the broomy lea,
And every fairy wheel and thread
Of cobweb dew-bediamonded.

When daisies go, shall winter time
Silver the simple grass with rime;
Autumnal frosts enchant the pool
And make the cart-ruts beautiful;
And when snow-bright the moor expands
How shall your children clap their hands!
To make this earth our hermitage,
A cheerful and a changeful page,
God's bright and intricate device
Of days and seasons doth suffice.

———

VI

A VISIT FROM THE SEA

Far from the loud sea beaches
  Where he goes fishing and crying,
Here in the inland garden
  Why is the sea-gull flying?

Here are no fish to dive for;
  Here is the corn and lea;
Here are the green trees rustling.
  Hie away home to sea!

Fresh is the river water
  And quiet among the rushes;

This is no home for the sea-gull
    But for the rooks and thrushes.

Pity the bird that has wandered!
    Pity the sailor ashore!
Hurry him home to the ocean,
    Let him come here no more.

High on the sea-cliff ledges
    The white gulls are trooping and
        crying,
Here among rooks and roses,
    Why is the sea-gull flying?

———

VII

TO A GARDENER

FRIEND, in my mountain-side demesne,
My plain-beholding, rosy, green
And linnet-haunted garden-ground,
Let still the esculents abound.
Let first the onion flourish there,
Rose among roots, the maiden-fair,
Wine-scented and poetic soul
Of the capacious salad bowl.

A THING THAT HAS NO WORTH UNTIL YOU LEND IT SOMETHING OF YOUR GRACE.

—Underwoods, Vol. Fifteen.

Let thyme the mountaineer (to dress
The tinier birds) and wading cress,
The lover of the shallow brook,
From all my plots and borders look.
Nor crisp and ruddy radish, nor
Pease-cods for the child's pinafore
Be lacking; nor of salad clan
The last and least that ever ran
About great nature's garden-beds.
Nor thence be missed the speary heads
Of artichoke; nor thence the bean
That gathered innocent and green
Outsavors the belauded pea.

These tend, I prithee; and for me,
Thy most long-suffering master, bring
In April, when the linnets sing
And the days lengthen more and more
At sundown to the garden door.
And I, being provided thus,
Shall, with superb asparagus,
A book, a taper, and a cup
Of country wine, divinely sup.

La Solitude, Hyères.

VIII

TO MINNIE

(With a Hand-Glass)

A PICTURE-FRAME for you to fill,
  A paltry setting for your face,
A thing that has no worth until
  You lend it something of your grace,

I send (unhappy I that sing
  Laid by a while upon the shelf)
Because I would not send a thing
  Less charming than you are yourself.

And happier than I, alas!
  (Dumb thing, I envy its delight),
'Twill wish you well, the looking-glass,
  And look you in the face to-night.

1869.

———

IX

TO K. de M.

A LOVER of the moorland bare
And honest country winds, you were;
The silver-skimming rain you took;
And loved the floodings of the brook,

Dew, frost and mountains, fire and seas,
Tumultuary silences,
Winds that in darkness fifed a tune,
And the high-riding, virgin moon.

And as the berry, pale and sharp,
Springs on some ditch's counterscarp
In our ungenial, native north—
You put your frosted wildings forth,
And on the heath, afar from man,
A strong and bitter virgin ran.

The berry ripened keeps the rude
And racy flavor of the wood;
And you that loved the empty plain
All redolent of wind and rain,
Around you still the curlew sings—
The freshness of the weather clings—
The maiden jewels of the rain
Sit in your dabbled locks again.

———

X

TO N. V. de G. S.

THE unfathomable sea, and time, and tears,
The deeds of heroes and the crimes of kings
Dispart us; and the river of events
Has, for an age of years, to east and west

More widely borne our cradles. Thou to me
Art foreign, as when seamen at the dawn
Descry a land far off and know not which.
So I approach uncertain; so I cruise
Round thy mysterious islet, and behold
Surf and great mountains and loud river-bars,
And from the shore hear inland voices call.
Strange is the seaman's heart; he hopes, he
      fears;
Draws closer and sweeps wider from that
      coast;
Last, his rent sail refits, and to the deep
His shattered prow uncomforted puts back.
Yet as he goes he ponders at the helm
Of that bright island; where he feared to
      touch,
His spirit re-adventures; and for years,
Where by his wife he slumbers safe at home,
Thoughts of that land revisit him; he sees
The eternal mountains beckon, and awakes
Yearning for that far home that might have
      been.

XI

TO WILL. H. LOW

YOUTH now flees on feathered foot
Faint and fainter sounds the flute,
Rarer songs of gods; and still
Somewhere on the sunny hill,
Or along the winding stream,
Through the willows, flits a dream;
Flits, but shows a smiling face,
Flees, but with so quaint a grace,
None can choose to stay at home,
All must follow, all must roam.
This is unborn beauty: she
Now in air floats high and free,
Takes the sun and breaks the blue;—
Late with stooping pinion flew
Raking hedgerow trees, and wet
Her wing in silver streams, and set
Shining foot on temple roof:
Now again she flies aloof,
Coasting mountain clouds and kiss't
By the evening's amethyst.

In wet wood and miry lane,
Still we pant and pound in vain;
Still with leaden foot we chase
Waning pinion, fainting face;

Still with gray hair we stumble on,
Till, behold, the vision gone!
Where hath fleeting beauty led?
To the doorway of the dead.
Life is over, life was gay:
We have come the primrose way.

———

XII

TO MRS. WILL. H. LOW

EVEN in the bluest noonday of July,
There could not run the smallest breath of wind
But all the quarter sounded like a wood;
And in the checkered silence and above
The hum of city cabs that sought the Bois,
Suburban ashes shivered into song.
A patter and a chatter and a chirp
And a long-dying hiss—it was as though
Starched old brocaded dames through all the
        house
Had trailed a strident skirt, or the whole sky
Even in a wink had over-brimmed in rain.
Hark, in these shady parlors, how it talks
Of the near autumn, how the smitten ash
Trembles and augurs floods! O not too long

In these inconstant latitudes delay,
O not too late from the unbeloved north
Trim your escape! For soon shall this low roof
Resound indeed with rain, soon shall your eyes
Search the foul garden, search the darkened
    rooms,
Nor find one jewel but the blazing log.

12 Rue Vernier, Paris.

XIII

TO H. F. BROWN

(Written During a Dangerous Sickness)

I sit and wait a pair of oars
On cis-Elysian river-shores.
Where the immortal dead have sate,
'Tis mine to sit and meditate;
To re-ascend life's rivulet,
Without remorse, without regret;
And sing my *Alma Genetrix*
Among the willows of the Styx.

And lo, as my serener soul
Did these unhappy shores patrol,
And wait with an attentive ear
The coming of the gondolier,

Your fire-surviving roll I took,
Your spirited and happy book;*
Whereon, despite my frowning fate,
It did my soul so recreate
That all my fancies fled away
On a Venetian holiday.

Now, thanks to your triumphant
    care,
Your pages clear as April air,
The sails, the bells, the birds, I
    know,
And the far-off Friulan snow;
The land and sea, the sun and
    shade,
And the blue even lamp-inlaid,
For this, for these, for all, O friend,
For your whole book from end to
    end—
For Paron Piero's muttonham—
I your defaulting debtor am.

Perchance, reviving, yet may I
To your sea-paven city hie,
And in a *felze*, some day yet
Light at your pipe my cigarette.

---

* "Life on the Lagoons," by H. F. Brown, originally burned in the fire at Messrs. Kegan Paul, Trench & Co.'s.

XIV

TO   ANDREW   LANG

DEAR Andrew, with the brindled hair,
Who glory to have thrown in air,
High over arm, the trembling reed,
By Ale and Kail, by Till and Tweed;
An equal craft of hand you show
The pen to guide, the fly to throw:
I count you happy starred; for God,
When He with inkpot and with rod
Endowed you, bade your fortune lead
Forever by the crooks of Tweed,
Forever by the woods of song
And lands that to the Muse belong;
Or if in peopled streets, or in
The abhorred pedantic sanhedrim,
It should be yours to wander, still
Airs of the morn, airs of the hill,
The plovery Forest and the seas
That break about the Hebrides,
Should follow over field and plain
And find you at the window-pane;
And you again see hill and peel,
And the bright springs gush at your
        heel.

So went the fiat forth, and so
Garrulous like a brook you go,
With sound of happy mirth and sheen
Of daylight—whether by the green
You fare that moment, or the gray;
Whether you dwell in March or May;
Or whether treat of reels and rods
Or of the old unhappy gods:
Still like a brook your page has shone,
And your ink sings of Helicon.

———

XV

ET TU IN ARCADIA VIXISTI

(TO R. A. M. S)

In ancient tales, O friend, thy spirit dwelt;
There, from of old, thy childhood passed; and
    there
High expectation, high delights and deeds,
Thy fluttering heart with hope and terror moved.
And thou hast heard of yore the Blatant Beast,
And Roland's horn, and that war-scattering shout
Of all-unarmed Achilles, ægis-crowned.
And perilous lands thou sawest, sounding shores
And seas and forests drear, island and dale

And mountain dark. For thou with Tristram
 rod'st
Or Bedevere, in farthest Lyonesse
Thou hadst a booth in Samarcand, whereat
Side-looking Magians trafficked; thence, by night,
An Afreet snatched thee, and with wings upbore
Beyond the Aral mount; or hoping gain,
Thou, with a jar of money didst embark
For Balsorah, by sea. But chiefly thou
In that clear air took'st life; in Arcady
The haunted, land of song; and by the wells
Where most the gods frequent. There Chiron
 old,
In the Pelethronian antre, taught thee lore :
The plants, he taught, and by the shining stars
In forests dim to steer. There hast thou seen
Immortal Pan dance secret in a glade,
And, dancing, roll his eyes; these where they
 fell,
Shed glee, and through the congregated oaks
A flying horror winged; while all the earth
To the god's pregnant footing thrilled within.
Or whiles, beside the sobbing stream, he breathed,
In his clutched pipe unformed and wizard
 strains
Divine yet brutal; which the forest heard,
And thou, with awe; and far upon the plain
The unthinking plowman started and gave ear.

Now things there are that, upon him who sees,
A strong vocation lay; and strains there are
That whoso hears shall hear for evermore.
For evermore thou hear'st a mortal Pan
And those melodious godheads, ever young
And ever quiring on the mountains old.

What was this earth, child of the gods, to thee?
Forth from thy dreamland thou, a dreamer cam'st
And in thine ears the olden music rang,
And in thy mind the doings of the dead,
And those heroic ages long forgot.
To a so fallen earth, alas! too late,
Alas! in evil days, thy steps return,
To list at noon for nightingales, to grow
A dweller on the beach till Argo come
That came long since, a lingerer by the pool
Where that desired angel bathes no more.

As when the Indian to Dakota comes
Or farthest Idaho, and where he dwelt,
He with his clan, a humming city finds;
Thereon a while, amazed, he stares, and then
To right and leftward, like a questing dog,
Seeks first the ancestral altars, then the hearth
Long cold with rains, and where old terror lodged,
And where the dead.   So thee undying Hope,
With all her pack, hunts screaming through the
      years:

Here, there, thou fleest; but nor here nor there
The pleasant gods abide, the glory dwells.

That, that was not Apollo, not the god.
This was not Venus, though she Venus seemed
A moment. And though fair yon river move,
She, all the way from disenchanted fount
To seas unhallowed runs; the gods forsook
Long since her trembling rushes; from her plains
Disconsolate, long since adventure fled;
And now although the inviting river flows
And every poplared cape and every bend
Or willowy islet, win upon thy soul
And to thy hopeful shallop whisper speed;
Yet hope not thou at all; hope is no more;
And O, long since the golden groves are dead
The faery cities vanished from the land!

XVI

TO W. E. HENLEY

THE year runs through her phases; rain and sun,
Springtime and summer pass; winter succeeds;
But one pale season rules the house of death.
Cold falls the imprisoned daylight; fell disease
By each lean pallet squats, and pain and sleep
Toss gaping on the pillows.

But O thou!
Uprise and take thy pipe. Bid music flow,
Strains by good thoughts attended, like the
        spring
The swallows follow over land and sea.
Pain sleeps at once; at once, with open eyes,
Dozing despair awakes. The shepherd sees
His flock come bleating home; the seaman hears
Once more the cordage rattle. Airs of home!
Youth, love and roses blossom; the gaunt ward
Dislimns and disappears, and, opening out,
Shows brooks and forests, and the blue beyond
Of mountains.

        Small the pipe; but oh! do thou,
Peak-faced and suffering piper, blow therein
The dirge of heroes dead; and to these sick,
These dying, sound the triumph over death.
Behold! each greatly breathes; each tastes a joy
Unknown before, in dying; for each knows
A hero dies with him—though unfulfilled,
Yet conquering truly—and not dies in vain

So is pain cheered, death comforted; the house
Of sorrow smiles to listen. Once again—
O thou, Orpheus and Heracles, the bard
And the deliverer, touch the stops again!

XVII

HENRY JAMES

WHO comes to-night?   We ope the doors in vain.
Who comes?   My bursting walls, can you contain
The presences that now together throng
Your narrow entry, as with flowers and song,
As with the air of life, the breath of talk?
Lo, how these fair immaculate women walk
Behind their jocund maker; and we see
Slighted *De Mauves*, and that far different she,
Gressie, the trivial sphynx; and to our feast
Daisy and *Barb* and *Chancellor* (she not least!)
With all their silken, all their airy kin,
Do like unbidden angels enter in.
But he, attended by these shining names,
Comes (best of all) himself—our welcome James.

XVIII

THE MIRROR SPEAKS

WHERE the bells peal far at sea
Cunning fingers fashioned me.
There on palace walls I hung
While that Consuelo sung;

But I heard, though I listened well,
Never a note, never a trill,
Never a beat of the chiming bell.
There I hung and looked, and there
In my gray face, faces fair
Shone from under shining hair.
Well I saw the poising head,
But the lips moved and nothing said;
And when lights were in the hall,
Silent moved the dancers all.

So a while I glowed, and then
Fell on dusty days and men;
Long I slumbered packed in straw,
Long I none but dealers saw;
Till before my silent eye
One that sees came passing by.

Now with an outlandish grace,
To the sparkling fire I face
In the blue room at Skerryvore;
Where I wait until the door
Open, and the Prince of Men,
Henry James, shall come again.

———

XIX

KATHARINE

WE see you as we see a face
That trembles in a forest place
Upon the mirror of a pool
Forever quiet, clear and cool;
And in the wayward glass appears
To hover between smiles and tears
Elfin and human, airy and true,
And backed by the reflected blue.

———

XX

TO F. J. S.

I READ, dear friend, in your dear face
Your life's tale told with perfect grace;
The river of your life I trace
Up the sun-checkered, devious bed
To the far-distant fountain-head.

Not one quick beat of your warm heart,
Nor thought that came to you apart,
Pleasure nor pity, love nor pain
Nor sorrow, has gone by in vain;

But as some lone, wood-wandering child
Brings home with him at evening mild
The thorns and flowers of all the wild,
From your whole life, O fair and true
Your flowers and thorns you bring with you!

———

XXI

REQUIEM

UNDER the wide and starry sky,
Dig the grave and let me lie.
Glad did I live and gladly die,
    And I laid me down with a will.

This be the verse you grave for me:
Here he lies where he longed to be;
Home is the sailor, home from sea,
    And the hunter home from the hill.

———

XXII

THE CELESTIAL SURGEON

IF I have faltered more or less
In my great task of happiness;
If I have moved among my race
And shown no glorious morning face;

If beams from happy human eyes
Have moved me not; if morning skies,
Books, and my food, and summer rain
Knocked on my sullen heart in vain:—
Lord, thy most pointed pleasure take
And stab my spirit broad awake;
Or, Lord, if too obdurate I,
Choose thou, before that spirit die,
A piercing pain, a killing sin,
And to my dead heart run them in!

XXIII

OUR LADY OF THE SNOWS

Out of the sun, out of the blast,
Out of the world, alone I passed
Across the moor and through the wood
To where the monastery stood.
There neither lute nor breathing fife,
Nor rumor of the world of life,
Nor confidences low and dear,
Shall strike the meditative ear.
Aloof, unhelpful, and unkind,
The prisoners of the iron mind,
Where nothing speaks except the hell
The unfraternal brothers dwell.

Poor, passionate men, still clothed afresh
With agonizing folds of flesh;
Whom the clear eyes solicit still
To some bold output of the will,
While fairy Fancy far before
And musing Memory-Hold-the-door
Now to heroic death invite
And now uncurtain fresh delight:
O, little boots it thus to dwell
On the remote unneighbored hill!

O, to be up and doing, O
Unfearing and unshamed to go
In all the uproar and the press
About my human business!
My undissuaded heart I hear
Whisper courage in my ear.
With voiceless calls, the ancient earth
Summons me to a daily birth.
Thou, O my love, ye, O my friends—
The gist of life, the end of ends—
To laugh, to love, to live, to die,
Ye call me by the ear and eye!

Forth from the casemate, on the plain
Where honor has the world to gain,
Pour forth and bravely do your part,
O knights of the unshielded heart!

Forth and forever forward!—out
From prudent turret and redoubt,
And in the mellay charge amain,
To fall, but yet to rise again!
Captive? ah, still, to honor bright,
A captive soldier of the right!
Or free and fighting, good with ill?
Unconquering but unconquered still!

And ye, O brethren, what if God,
When from heav'n's top he spies
    abroad,
And sees on this tormented stage
The noble war of mankind rage:
What if his vivifying eye,
O monks, should pass your corner by?
For still the Lord is Lord of might;
In deeds, in deeds, he takes delight;
The plow, the spear, the laden barks,
The field, the founded city, marks;
He marks the smiler of the streets,
The singer upon garden seats;
He sees the climber in the rocks:
To him the shepherd folds his flocks.
For those he loves that underprop
With daily virtues heaven's top,
And bear the falling sky with ease,
Unfrowning caryatides.

Those he approves that ply the trade,
That rock the child, that wed the maid,
That with weak virtues, weaker hands,
Sow gladness on the peopled lands,
And still with laughter, song and shout,
Spin the great wheel of earth about.

But ye?—O ye who linger still,
Here in your fortress on the hill,
With placid face, with tranquil breath,
The unsought volunteers of death,
Our cheerful General on high
With careless looks may pass you by.

XXIV

NOT yet, my soul, these friendly fields desert,
Where thou with grass, and rivers, and the breeze,
And the bright face of day, thy dalliance hadst;
Where to thine ear first sang the enraptured
        birds;
Where love and thou that lasting bargain made.
The ship rides trimmed, and from the eternal
        shore
Thou hearest airy voices; but not yet
Depart, my soul, not yet a while depart.

Freedom is far, rest far. Thou art with life
Too closely woven, nerve with nerve entwined;
Service still craving service, love for love,
Love for dear love, still suppliant with tears.
Alas, not yet thy human task is done!
A bond at birth is forged; a debt doth lie
Immortal on mortality. It grows—
By vast rebound it grows, unceasing growth;
Gift upon gift, alms upon alms, upreared,
From man, from God, from nature, till the soul
At that so huge indulgence stands amazed.

Leave not, my soul, the unfoughten field, nor
    leave
Thy debts dishonored, nor thy place desert
Without due service rendered. For thy life,
Up, spirit, and defend that fort of clay,
Thy body, now beleaguered; whether soon
Or late she fall; whether to-day thy friends
Bewail thee dead, or, after years, a man
Grown old in honor and the friend of peace.
Contend, my soul, for moments and for hours;
Each is with service pregnant; each reclaimed
Is as a kingdom conquered, where to reign.
As when a captain rallies to the fight
His scattered legions, and beats ruin back,
He, on the field, encamps, well pleased in mind.
Yet surely him shall fortune overtake,

Him smite in turn, headlong his ensigns drive;
And that dear land, now safe, to-morrow fall.
But he, unthinking, in the present good
Solely delights, and all the camps rejoice.

———

XXV

It is not yours, O mother, to complain,
Not, mother, yours to weep,
Though nevermore your son again
Shall to your bosom creep,
Though nevermore again you watch your
        baby sleep.

Though in the greener paths of earth,
Mother and child no more
We wander; and no more the birth
Of me whom once you bore
Seems still the brave reward that once it
        seemed of yore;

Though as all passes, day and night,
The seasons and the years,
From you, O mother, this delight,
This also disappears—
Some profit yet survives of all your pangs
        and tears.

WHY AM I LYING AWAKE SO LATE?
—Underwoods, Vol. Fifteen.

The child, the seed, the grain of corn,
The acorn on the hill,
Each for some separate end is born
In season fit, and still
Each must in strength arise to work the
    almighty will.

So from the hearth the children flee,
By that almighty hand
Austerely led; so one by sea
Goes forth, and one by land;
Nor aught of all man's sons escape from
    that command.

So from the sally each obeys
The unseen almighty nod;
So till the ending all their ways
Blindfolded loth have trod:
Nor knew their task at all, but were the
    tools of God.

And as the fervent smith of yore
Beat out the glowing blade,
Nor wielded in the front of war
The weapons that he made,
But in the tower at home still plied his
    ringing trade;

So like a sword the son shall roam
On nobler missions sent;

And as the smith remained at home
In peaceful turret pent,
So sits the while at home the mother
    well content.

––––

XXVI

THE SICK CHILD

Child

O MOTHER, lay your hand on my brow!
O mother, mother, where am I now?
Why is the room so gaunt and great?
Why am I lying awake so late?

Mother

Fear not at all: the night is still;
Nothing is here that means you ill—
Nothing but lamps the whole town through,
And never a child awake but you.

Child

Mother, mother, speak low in my ear,
Some of the things are so great and near,
Some are so small and far away,
I have a fear that I cannot say.
What have I done, and what do I fear,
And why are you crying, mother dear?

Mother
 Out in the city, sounds begin
 Thank the kind God, the carts come in!
 An hour or two more, and God is so kind,
 The day shall be blue in the window-blind,
 Then shall my child go sweetly asleep,
 And dream of the birds and the hills of
  sheep.

———

XXVII

IN MEMORIAM F. A. S.

YET, O stricken heart, remember, O remember
 How of human days he lived the better part.
April came to bloom and never dim December
 Breathed its killing chills upon the head or
  heart.

Doomed to know not Winter, only Spring, a
  being
 Trod the flowery April blithely for a while,
Took his fill of music, joy of thought and
  seeing,
 Came and stayed and went, nor ever ceased
  to smile.

Came and stayed and went, and now when all
        is finished,
    You alone have crossed the melancholy stream,
Yours the pang, but his, O his, the undiminished
    Undecaying gladness, undeparted dream.

All that life contains of torture, toil, and treason,
    Shame, dishonor, death, to him were but a
        name.
Here, a boy, he dwelt through all the singing
        season
    And ere the day of sorrow departed as he
        came.

Davos, 1881.

————

XXVIII

TO MY FATHER

PEACE and her huge invasion to these shores
Puts daily home; innumerable sails
Dawn on the far horizon and draw near;
Innumerable loves, uncounted hopes
To our wild coasts, not darkling now, approach:
Not now obscure, since thou and thine are there,
And bright on the lone isle, the foundered reef,
The long, resounding foreland, Pharos stands.

These are thy works, O father, these thy crown;
Whether on high the air be pure, they shine
Along the yellowing sunset, and all night
Among the unnumbered stars of God they shine;
Or whether fogs arise and far and wide
The low sea-level drown—each finds a tongue
And all night long the tolling bell resounds:
So shine, so toll, till night be overpast,
Till the stars vanish, till the sun return,
And in the haven rides the fleet secure.

In the first hour, the seaman in his skiff
Moves through the unmoving bay, to where the
town
Its earliest smoke into the air upbreathes
And the rough hazels climb along the beach.
To the tugg'd oar the distant echo speaks.
The ship lies resting, where by reef and roost
Thou and thy lights have led her like a child.

This hast thou done, and I—can I be base?
I must arise, O father, and to port
Some lost, complaining seaman pilot home.

XXIX

IN THE STATES

WITH half a heart I wander here
　　As from an age gone by　.
A brother—yet though young in years,
　　An elder brother, I.

You speak another tongue than mine,
　　Though both were English born.
I toward the night of time decline,
　　You mount into the morn.

Youth shall grow great and strong and
　　　　free,
　　But age must still decay:
To-morrow for the States—for me,
　　England and Yesterday.

San Francisco.

———

XXX

A PORTRAIT

I AM a kind of farthing dip,
　　Unfriendly to the nose and eyes;
A blue-behinded ape, I skip
　　Upon the trees of Paradise.

At mankind's feast, I take my place
   In solemn, sanctimonious state,
And have the air of saying grace
   While I defile the dinner-plate.

I am "the smiler with the knife,"
   The battener upon garbage, I—
Dear Heaven, with such a rancid life,
   Were it not better far to die?

Yet still, about the human pale,
   I love to scamper, love to race,
To swing by my irreverent tail
   All over the most holy place;

And when at length, some golden day,
   The unfailing sportsman, aiming at,
Shall bag, me—all the world shall say,
   Thank God, and there's an end of that!

XXXI

Sing clearlier, Muse, or evermore be still,
Sing truer or no longer sing!
No more the voice of melancholy Jacques
To wake a weeping echo in the hill;
But as the boy, the pirate of the spring,
From the green elm a living linnet takes,
One natural verse recapture—then be still.

XXXII

A CAMP*

THE bed was made, the room was fit
By punctual eve the stars were lit;
The air was still, the water ran,
No need was there for maid or man,
When we put up, my ass and I,
At God's green caravanserai.

XXXIII

THE COUNTRY OF THE CAMISARDS†

WE traveled in the print of olden wars,
    Yet all the land was green
    And love we found, and peace,
    Where fire and war had been.

They pass and smile, the children of the sword—
    No more the sword they wield;
    And O, how deep the corn
    Along the battlefield!

---

* From "Travels with a Donkey."   † Ibid.

XXXIV

SKERRYVORE

For love of lovely words and for the sake
Of those, my kinsmen and my countrymen,
Who early and late in the windy ocean toiled
To plant a star for seamen, where was then
The surfy haunt of seals and cormorants:
I, on the lintel of this cot, inscribe
The name of a strong tower.

XXXV

SKERRYVORE: The Parallel

Here all is sunny, and when the truant gull
Skims the green level of the lawn, his wing
Dispetals roses; here the house is framed
Of kneaded brick and the plumed mountain pine,
Such clay as artists fashion and such wood
As the tree-climbing urchin breaks   But there
Eternal granite hewn from the living isle
And dowelled with brute iron, rears a tower
That from its wet foundation to its crown
Of glittering glass, stands, in the sweep of
    winds,
Immovable, immortal, eminent.

XXXVI

My house, I say.   But hark to the sunny doves
That make my roof the arena of their loves,
That gyre about the gable all day long
And fill the chimneys with their murmurous
    song:
Our house, they say; and *mine*, the cat declares
And spreads his golden fleece upon the chairs;
And *mine*, the dog, and rises stiff with wrath
If any alien foot profane the path.
So too the buck that trimmed my terraces,
Our whilome gardener, called the garden his;
Who now, deposed, surveys my plain abode
And his late kingdom, only from the road.

XXXVII

My body which my dungeon is,
  And yet my parks and palaces:—
    Which is so great that there I go
All the day long to and fro,
And when the night begins to fall
Throw down my bed and sleep, while all
The building hums with wakefulness—
Even as a child of savages

When evening takes her on her way,
(She having roamed a summer's day
Along the mountain-sides and scalp)
Sleeps in an antre of that alp:—
   Which is so broad and high that there,
As in the topless fields of air,
My fancy soars like to a kite
And faints in the blue infinite:—
   Which is so strong, my strongest throes
And the rough world's besieging blows
Not break it, and so weak withal,
Death ebbs and flows in its loose wall
As the green sea in fishers' nets,
And tops its topmost parapets:—
   Which is so wholly mine that I
Can wield its whole artillery,
And mine so little, that my soul
Dwells in perpetual control,
And I but think and speak and do
As my dead fathers move me to:—
   If this born body of my bones
The beggared soul so barely owns,
What money passed from hand to hand,
What creeping custom of the land,
What deed of author or assign,
Can make a house a thing of mine?

XXXVIII

Say not of me that weakly I declined
The labors of my sires, and fled the sea,
The towers we founded and the lamps we lit,
To play at home with paper like a child.
But rather say: *In the afternoon of time*
A strenuous family dusted from its hands
The sand of granite, and beholding far
Along the sounding coast its pyramids
And tall memorials catch the dying sun,
Smiled well content, and to this childish task
Around the fire addressed its evening hours.

BOOK II — IN SCOTS

TABLE OF COMMON SCOTTISH VOWEL SOUNDS

ae }
ai } = open A as in rare.

a' }
au } = AW as in law.
aw }

ea = open E as in mere, but this with exceptions, as heather = heather, wean = wain, lear = lair.

ee }
ei } = open E as in mere.
ie }

oa = open O as in more.

ou = doubled O as in poor.

ow = OW as in Bower.

u = doubled O as in poor.

ui or ü before R = (say roughly) open A as in rare.

ui or ü before any other consonant = (say roughly) close I as in grin.

y = open I as in kite.

i = pretty nearly what you please, much as in English. Heaven guide the reader through that labyrinth! But in Scots it dodges usually from the short I, as in grin, to the open E, as in mere. Find and blind, I may remark, are pronounced to rhyme with the preterite of grin.

I

THE MAKER TO POSTERITY

Far 'yont amang the years to be
When a' we think, an' a' we see,
An' a' we luve, 's been dung ajee
  By time's rouch shouther,
An' what was richt and wrang for me
  Lies mangled throu'ther,

It's possible—it's hardly mair—
That some ane, ripin' after lear—
Some auld professor or young heir,
  If still there's either—
May find an' read me, an' be sair
  Perplexed, puir brither!

"What tongue does your auld bookie speak?"
He'll spier; an' I, his mou to steik:
"No bein' fit to write in Greek,
  I wrote in Lallan,
Dear to my heart as the peat reek,
  Auld as Tantallon.

"Few spak it than, an' noo there's nane.
My puir auld sangs lie a' their lane,
Their sense, that aince was braw an' plain,
  Tint a'thegether,
Like runes upon a standin' stane
  Amang the heather.

"But think not you the brae to speel;
You, tae, maun chow the bitter peel;
For a' your lear, for a' your skeel,
  Ye're nane sae lucky;
An' things are mebbe waur than weel
  For you, my buckie.

"The hale concern (baith hens an' eggs,
Baith books an' writers, stars an' clegs)
Noo stachers upon lowsent legs
  An' wears awa';
The tack o' mankind, near the dregs,
  Rins unco law.

"Your book, that in some braw new tongue,
Ye wrote or prentit, preached or sung,
Will still be just a bairn, an' young
  In fame an' years,
Whan the hale planet's guts are dung
  About your ears;

"An' you, sair gruppin' to a spar
Or whammled wi' some bleezin' star,

Cryin' to ken whaur deil ye are,
  Hame, France, or Flanders—
Whang sindry like a railway car
  An' flie in danders."

———

II

ILLE TERRARUM

Frae nirly, nippin', Eas'lan' breeze,
Frae Norlan' snaw, an' haar o' seas,
Weel happit in your gairden trees,
  A bonny bit,
Atween the muckle Pentland's knees,
  Secure ye sit.

Beeches an' aiks entwine their theek,
An' firs, a stench, auld-farrant clique.
A' simmer day, your chimleys reek,
  Couthy and bien;
An' here an' there your windies keek
  Amang the green.

A pickle plats an' paths an' posies,
A wheen auld gillyflowers an' roses:
A ring o' wa's the hale incloses
  Frae sheep or men;
An' there the auld housie beeks an' dozes
  A' by her lane.

The gairdner crooks his weary back
A' day in the pitaty-track,
Or mebbe stops a while to crack
    Wi' Jane the cook,
Or at some buss, worm-eaten-black,
    To gie a look.

Frae the high hills the curlew ca's;
The sheep gang baaing by the wa's;
Or whiles a clan o' roosty craws
    Cangle together;
The wild bees seek the gairden raws,
    Weariet wi' heather.

Or in the gloamin' douce an' gray
The sweet-throat mavis tunes her lay;
The herd comes linkin' doun the brae;
    An' by degrees
The muckle siller müne maks way
    Amang the trees.

Here aft hae I, wi' sober heart,
For meditation sat apairt,
When orra loves or kittle art
    Perplexed my mind;
Here socht a balm for ilka smart
    O' humankind.

Here aft, weel neukit by my lane,
Wi' Horace, or perhaps Montaigne,

The mornin' hours hae come an' gane
　　　　Abüne my heid—
I wadnae gi'en a chucky-stane
　　　　For a' I'd read.

But noo the auld city, street by street,
An' winter fu' o' snaw an' sleet,
A while shut in my gangrel feet
　　　　An' goavin' mettle;
Noo is the soopit ingle sweet,
　　　　An' liltin' kettle.

An' noo the winter winds complain;
Cauld lies the glaur in ilka lane;
On draigled hizzie, tautit wean
　　　　An' drucken lads,
In the mirk nicht, the winter rain
　　　　Dribbles an' blads.

Whan bugles frae the Castle rock,
An' beaten drums wi' dowie shock,
Wauken, at cauld-rife sax o'clock,
　　　　My chitterin' frame,
I mind me on the kintry cock,
　　　　The kintry hame.

I mind me on yon bonny bield;
An' Fancy traivels far afield

To gaither a' that gairdens yield
    O' sun an' Simmer:
To hearten up a dowie chield,
    Fancy's the limmer!

III

WHEN aince Aprile has fairly come,
An' birds may bigg in winter's lum,
An' pleisure's spreid for a' and some
    O' whatna state,
Love, wi' her auld recruitin' drum,
    Than taks the gate.

The heart plays dunt wi' main an'
    micht;
The lasses' een are a' sae bricht,
Their dresses are sae braw an' ticht,
    The bonny birdies!—
Puir winter virtue at the sicht
    Gangs heels ower hurdies.

An' aye as love frae land to land
Tirls the drum wi' eident hand,
A' men collect at her command,
    Toun-bred or land'art,
An' follow in a denty band
    Her gaucy standart.

An' I, wha sang o' rain an' snaw,
An' weary winter weel awa',
Noo busk me in a jacket braw,
    An' tak my place
I' the ram-stam, harum-scarum raw,
    Wi' smilin' face.

———

IV

A MILE AN' A BITTOCK

A MILE an' a bittock, a mile or twa,
Abüne the burn, ayont the law,
Davie an' Donal' an' Cherlie an' a',
    An' the müne was shinin' clearly!

Ane went hame wi' the ither, an' then
The ither went hame wi' the ither twa men,
An' baith wad return him the service again,
    An' the müne was shinin' clearly!

The clocks were chappin' in house an' ha',
Eleeven, twal an' ane an' twa;
An' the guidman's face was turnt to the wa',
    An' the müne was shinin' clearly!

A wind got up frae affa the sea,
It blew the stars as clear's could be,
It blew in the een of a' o' the three,
    An' the müne was shinin' clearly!

Noo, Davie was first to get sleep in his head,
" The best o' frien's maun twine," he said;
" I'm weariet, an' here I'm awa' to my bed."
         An' the müne was shinin' clearly!

Twa o' them walkin' an' crackin' their lane,
The mornin' licht cam gray an' plain,
An' the birds they yammert on stick an'
    stane,
         An' the müne was shinin' clearly!

O years ayont, O years awa',
My lads, ye'll mind whate'er befa'—
My lads, ye'll mind on the bield o' the law,
         When the müne was shinin' clearly.

———

V

A LOWDEN SABBATH MORN

THE clinkum-clank o' Sabbath bells
Noo to the hoastin' rookery swells,
Noo faintin' laigh in shady dells,
         Sounds far an' near,
An' through the simmer kintry tells
         Its tale o' cheer.

An' noo, to that melodious play,
A' deidly awn the quiet sway—
A' ken their solemn holiday,
  Bestial an' human,
The singin' lintie on the brae,
  The restin' plou'man.

He, mair than a' the lave o' men,
His week completit joys to ken;
Half-dressed, he daunders out an' in,
  Perplext wi' leisure;
An' his raxt limbs he'll rax again
  Wi' painfü' pleesure.

The steerin' mither strang afit
Noo shoos the bairnies but a bit;
Noo cries them ben, their Sinday shüit
  To scart upon them,
Or sweeties in their pouch to pit,
  Wi' blessin's on them.

The lasses, clean frae tap to taes,
Are busked in crunklin' underclaes;
The gartened hose, the weel-filled stays,
  The nakit shift,
A' bleached on bonny greens for days,
  An' white's the drift.

An' noo to face the kirkward mile:
The guidman's hat o' dacent style,

The blackit shoon, we noo maun fyle
    As white's the miller:
A waefü' peety tae, to spile
    The warth o' siller.

Our Marg'et, aye sae keen to crack,
Douce-stappin' in the stoury track,
Her emeralt goun a' kiltit back
    Frae snawy coats,
White-ankled, leads the kirkward pack
    Wi' Dauvit Groats.

A thocht ahint, in runkled breeks
A' spiled wi' lyin' by for weeks,
The guidman follows closs, an' cleiks
    The sonsie missis;
His sarious face at aince bespeaks
    The day that this is.

And aye an' while we nearer draw
To whaur the kirton lies alaw,
Mair neebors, comin' saft an' slaw
    Frae here an' there,
The thicker thrang the gate an' caw
    The stour in air.

But hark! the bells frae nearer clang;
To rowst the slaw, their sides they
    bang;

An' see! black coats a'ready thrang
　　The green kirkyaird,
And at the yett, the chestnuts spang
　　That brocht the laird.

The solemn elders at the plate
Stand drinkin' deep the pride o' state:
That practiced hands as gash an' great
　　As Lords o' Session;
The later named, a wee thing blate
　　In their expression.

The prentit stanes that mark the deid,
Wi' lengthened lip, the sarious read;
Syne wag a moraleesin' heid,
　　An' then an' there
Their hirplin' practice an' their creed
　　Try hard to square.

It's here our Merren lang has lain,
A wee bewast the table-stane;
An' yon's the grave o' Sandy Blane;
　　An' further ower,
The mither's brithers, dacent men!
　　Lie a' the fower.

Here the guidman sall bide awee
To dwall amang the deid; to see

Auld faces clear in fancy's e'e;
    Belike to hear
Auld voices fa'in' saft an' slee
    On fancy's ear.

Thus, on the day o' solemn things,
The bell that in the steeple swings
To fauld a scaittered faim'ly rings
    Its walcome screed;
An' just a wee thing nearer brings
    The quick an' deid.

But noo the bell is ringin' in;
To tak their places, folk begin;
The minister himsel' will shüne
    Be up the gate,
Filled fu' wi' clavers about sin
    An' man's estate.

The tünes are up—*French*, to be shüre,
The faithfü' *French*, an' twa-three mair·
The auld prezentor, hoastin' sair,
    Wales out the portions,
An' yirks the tüne into the air
    Wi' queer contortions.

Follows the prayer, the readin' next,
An' than the fisslin' for the text—

The twa-three last to find it, vext
But kind o' proud;
An' than the peppermints are raxed,
An' southernwood.

For noo's the time whan pows are
seen
Nid-noddin' like a mandareen;
When tenty mithers stap a preen
In sleepin' weans;
An' nearly half the parochine
Forget their pains.

There's just a waukrif' twa or three:
Thrawn commentautors sweer to 'gree,
Weans glowrin' at the bumblin' bee
On windie-glasses,
Or lads that tak a keek a-glee
At sonsie lasses.

Himsel', meanwhile, frae whaur he cocks
An' bobs belaw the soundin'-box,
The treesures of his words unlocks
Wi' prodigality,
An' deals some unco dingin' knocks
To infidality.

Wi' sappy unction, hoo he burkes
The hopes o' men that trust in works,

Expounds the fau'ts o' ither kirks,
    An' shaws the best o' them
No muckle better than mere Turks,
    When a's confessed o' them.

Bethankit! what a bonny creed!
What mair would ony Christian need?—
The braw words rumm'le ower his heid,
    Nor steer the sleeper;
An' in their restin' graves, the deid
    Sleep aye the deeper.

NOTE.—It may be guessed by some that I had a certain parish in my eye, and this makes it proper I should add a word of disclamation. In my time there have been two ministers in that parish. Of the first I have a special reason to speak well, even had there been any to think ill. The second I have often met in private and long (in the due phrase) "sat under" in his church, and neither here nor there have I heard an unkind or ugly word upon his lips. The preacher of the text had thus no original in that particular parish; but when I was a boy, he might have been observed in many others; he was then (like the schoolmaster) abroad; and by recent advices, it would seem he has not yet entirely disappeared.

VI

THE SPAEWIFE

O, I wad like to ken—to the beggar-wife says I—
Why chops are guid to brander and nane sae
    guid to fry.
An' siller, that's sae braw to keep, is brawer still
    to gi'e.
—*It's gey an' easy spierin'*, says the beggar-wife
    to me.

O, I wad like to ken—to the beggar-wife says I—
Hoo a' things come to be whaur we find them
    when we try,
The lasses in their claes an' the fishes in the sea.
—*It's gey an' easy spierin'*, says the beggar-wife
    to me.

O, I wad like to ken—to the beggar-wife says I—
Why lads are a' to sell an' lasses a' to buy;
An' naebody for dacency but barely twa or three
—*It's gey an' easy spierin'*, says the beggar-wife
    to me.

O, I wad like to ken—to the beggar-wife says I—
Gin death's as shüre to men as killin' is to kye,
Why God has filled the yearth sae fu' o' tasty
    things to pree.
—*It's gey an' easy spierin'*, says the beggar-wife
    to me.

O, I wad like to ken—to the beggar-wife says I—
The reason o' the cause an' the wherefore o' the
    why,
Wi' mony anither riddle brings the tear into
    my e'e.
—*It's gey an' easy speirin'*, says the beggar-wife
    to me.

VII

THE BLAST—1875

It's rainin'. Weet's the gairden sod
Weet the lang roads whaur gangrels plod—
A maist unceevil thing o' God
    In mid July—
If ye'll just curse the sneckdraw, dod!
    An' sae wull I!

He's a braw place in heev'n, ye ken,
An' lea's us puir, forjaskit men
Clamjamfried in the but and ben
    He ca's the earth—
A wee bit inconvenient den
    No muckle worth;

An' whiles, at orra times, keeks out,
Sees what puir mankind are about;

An' if He can, I've little doubt,
    Upsets their plans;
He hates a' mankind, brainch and root,
    An' a' that's man's.

An' whiles, whan they tak heart again,
An' life i' the sun looks braw an' plain,
Doun comes a jaw o' droukin' rain
    Upon their honors—
God sends a spate outower the plain,
    Or mebbe thun'ers.

Lord safe us, life's an unco thing!
Simmer an' Winter, Yule an' Spring,
The damned, dour-heartit seasons bring
    A feck o' trouble.
I wadna try't to be a king—
    No, nor for double.

But since we're in it, willy-nilly,
We maun be watchfü', wise an' skilly
An' no mind ony ither billy,
    Lassie nor God.
But drink—that's my best counsel till 'e:
    Sae tak the nod.

VIII

THE COUNTERBLAST—1886

My bonny man, the warld, it's true,
Was made for neither me nor you;
It's just a place to warstle through,
      As Job confessed o't;
And aye the best that we'll can do
      Is mak the best o't.

There's rowth o' wrang, I'm free to say:
The simmer brunt, the winter blae,
The face of earth a' fyled wi' clay
      An' dour wi' chuckies,
An' life a rough an' land'art play
      For country buckies.

An' food's anither name for clart;
An' beasts an' brambles bite an' scart;
An' what would WE be like, my heart!
      If bared o' claethin'?
—Aweel, I cannae mend your cart:
      It's that or naethin'.

A feck o' folk frae first to last
Have through this queer experience passed;
Twa-three, I ken, just damn an' blast
      The hale transaction;
But twa-three ithers, east an' wast,
      Fand satisfaction.

Whaur braid the briery muirs expand,
A waefü' an' a weary land,
The bumblebees, a gowden band,
      Are blithely hingin';
An' there the canty wanderer fand
      The laverock singin'.

Trout in the burn grow great as herr'n',
The simple sheep can find their fair'n';
The wind blaws clean about the cairn
      Wi' caller air;
The muircock an' the barefit bairn
      Are happy there.

Sic-like the howes o' life to some:
Green loans whaur they ne'er fash their
    thumb,
But mark the muckle winds that come.
      Soopin' an' cool,
Or hear the powrin' burnie drum
      In the shilfa's pool.

The evil wi' the guid they tak;
They ca' a gray thing gray, no black;
To a steigh brae, a stubborn back
      Addressin' daily;
An' up the rude, unbieldy track
      O' life, gang gayly.

What you would like's a palace ha',
Or Sinday parlor dink an' braw
Wi' a' things ordered in a raw
  By denty leddies.
Weel, than, ye cannae hae't: that's a'
  That to be said is.

An' since at life ye've taen the grue,
An' winnae blithely hirsle through,
Ye've fund the very thing to do—
  That's to drink speerit;
An' shüne we'll hear the last o' you—
  An' blithe to hear it!

The shoon ye coft, the life ye lead,
Ithers will heir when aince ye're deid;
They'll heir your tasteless bite o' breid,
  An' find it sappy;
They'll to your dulefü' house succeed,
  An' there be happy.

As whan a glum an' fractious wean
Has sat an' sullened by his lane
Till, wi' a rowstin' skelp, he's taen
  An' shoo'd to bed—
The ither bairns a' fa' to play'n',
  As gleg's a gled.

———

IX

THE COUNTERBLAST IRONICAL

It's strange that God should fash to frame
  The yearth and lift sae hie,
An' clean forget to explain the same
  To a gentleman like me.

They gutsy, donnered ither folk,
  Their weird they weel may dree;
But why present a pig in a poke
  To a gentleman like me?

They ither folk their parritch eat
  An' sup their sugared tea;
But the mind is no to be wyled wi' meat
  Wi' a gentleman like me.

They ither folk, they court their joes
  At gloamin' on the lea;
But they're made of a commoner clay, I suppose,
  Than a gentleman like me.

They ither folk, for richt or wrang,
  They suffer, bleed, or dee;
But a' thir things are an emp'y sang
  To a gentleman like me.

It's a different thing that I demand,
　　Tho' humble as can be—
A statement fair in my Maker's hand
　　To a gentleman like me:

A clear account writ fair an' broad,
　　An' a plain apologie;
Or the deevil a ceevil word to God
　　From a gentleman like me.

X

THEIR LAUREATE TO AN ACADEMY CLASS DINNER CLUB

DEAR Thamson class, whaure'er I gang
It aye comes ower me wi' a spang:
"Lordsake! they Thamson lads—(deil hang
　　　　Or else Lord mend them!)—
An' that wanchancy annual sang
　　　　I ne'er can send them!"

Straucht, at the name a trusty tyke,
My conscience girrs ahint the dyke;
Straucht on my hinderlands I fyke
　　　　To find a rhyme t' ye;
Pleased—although mebbe no pleased-like—
　　　　To gie my time t' ye.

"Weel," an' says you, wi' heavin' breist,
"Sae far, sae guid, but what's the neist?
Yearly we gaither to the feast,
    A' hopefu' men—
Yearly we skelloch 'Hang the beast—
        Nae sang again!'"

My lads, an' what am I to say?
Ye shürely ken the Muse's way:
Yestreen, as gleg's a tyke—the day,
        Thrawn like a cuddy:
Her conduc', that to her's a play,
        Deith to a body.

Aft whan I sat an' made my mane,
Aft whan I labored burd-alane
Fishin' for rhymes an' findin' nane,
        Or nane were fit for ye—
Ye judged me cauld's a chucky stane—
        No car'n' a bit for ye!

But saw ye ne'er some pingein' bairn
As weak as a pitaty-par'n'—
Less üsed wi' guidin' horse-shoe airn
        Than steerin' crowdie—
Packed aff his lane, by moss an' cairn,
        To ca' the howdie.

Wae's me, for the puir callant than!
He wambles like a poke o' bran,

An' the lowse rein, as hard's he can,
        Pu's, trem'lin' handit;
Till, blaff! upon his hinderlan'
        . Behauld him landit.

Sic-like—I awn the weary fac'—
Whan on my muse the gate I tak,
An' see her gleed e'e raxin' back
        To keek ahint her;—
To me the brig of heev'n gangs black
        As blackest winter.

"Lordsake! we're aff," thinks ·I, *"but whaur?*
On what abhorred and whinny scaur,
Or whammled in what sea o' glaur,
        Will she desert me?
An' will she just disgrace? or waur—
        Will she no hurt me?"

Kittle the quaere! But at least
The day I've backed the fashious beast,
While she, wi' mony a spang an' reist,
        Flang heels ower bonnet;
An' a' triumphant—for your feast,
        Hae! there's your sonnet!

XI

EMBRO HIE KIRK

THE Lord Himsel' in former days
Waled out the proper tünes for praise
An' named the proper kind o' claes
    For folk to preach in:
Preceese and in the chief o' ways
      Important teachin'.

He ordered a' things, late and air';
He ordered folk to stand at prayer
(Although I cannae just mind where
      He gave the warnin'),
An' pit pomatum on their hair
      On Sabbath mornin'.

The hale o' life by His commands
Was ordered to a body's hands;
But see! this *corpus juris* stands
      By a' forgotten;
An' God's religion in a' lands
      Is deid an' rotten.

While thus the lave o' mankind's lost,
O' Scotland still God maks his boast—

Puir Scotland, on whase barren coast
   A score or twa
Auld wives wi' mutches an' a hoast
   Still keep His law.

In Scotland, a wheen canty, plain,
Douce kintry-leevin' folk retain
The Truth—or did so aince—alane
   Of a' men leevin';
An' noo just twa o' them remain—
   Just Begg an' Niven.

For noo, unfaithfü' to the Lord
Auld Scotland joins the rebel horde;
Her human hymn-books on the board
   She noo displays:
An' Embro Hie Kirk's been restored
   In popish ways.

O *punctum temporis* for action
To a' o' the reformin' faction,
If yet, by ony act or paction,
   Thocht, word, or sermon,
This dark an' damnable transaction
   Micht yet determine!

For see—as Doctor Begg explains—
Hoo easy 't's düne! a pickle weans,

Wha in the Hie Street gaither stanes
  By his instruction,
The uncovenantit, pentit panes
  Ding to destruction.

Up, Niven, or ower late—an' dash
Laigh in the glaur that carnal hash;
Let spires and pews wi' gran' stramash
    Thegether fa';
The rumlin' kist o' whustles smash
    In pieces sma'.

Noo choose ye out a walie hammer;
About the knottit buttress clam'er;
Alang the steep roof stoyt an' stammer,
    A gate mis-chancy;
On the aul' spire, the bells' hie cha'mer,
    Dance your bit dancie.

Ding, devel, dunt, destroy, an' ruin,
Wi' carnal stanes the square bestrewin',
Till your loud chaps frae Kyle to Fruin,
    Frae hell to heeven,
Tell the guid wark that baith are doin'—
    Baith Begg an' Niven.

XII

THE SCOTSMAN'S RETURN FROM ABROAD

(In a letter from Mr. Thomson to Mr. Johnstone)

In mony a foreign pairt I've been,
An' mony an unco ferlie seen,
Since, Mr. Johnstone, you and I
Last walkit upon Cocklerye.
Wi' gleg, observant een, I pass't
By sea an' land, through East an' Wast,
And still in ilka age an' station
Saw naething but abomination.
In thir uncovenantit lands
The gangrel Scot uplifts his hands
At lack of a' sectarian füsh'n,
An' cauld religious destitütion.
He rins, puir man, frae place to place,
Tries a' their graceless means o' grace,
Preacher on preacher, kirk on kirk—
This yin a stot an' thon a stirk—
A bletherin' clan, no warth a preen,
As bad as Smith of Aiberdeen!

At last, across the weary faem,
Frae far, outlandish pairts I came.
On ilka side o' me I fand
Fresh tokens o' my native land.

Wi' whatna joy I hailed them a'—
The hilltaps standin' raw by raw,
The public house, the Hielan' birks,
And a' the bonny U. P. kirks!
But maistly thee, the bluid o' Scots,
Frae Maidenkirk to John o' Grots,
The king o' drinks, as I conceive it,
Talisker, Isla, or Glenlivet!

For after years wi' a pockmantie
Frae Zanzibar to Alicante,
In mony a fash an' sair affliction
I gie't as my sincere conviction—
Of a' their foreign tricks an' pliskies,
I maist abominate their whiskies.
Nae doot, themsel's, they ken it weel,
An' wi' a hash o' leemon peel,
An' ice an' siccan filth, they ettle
The stawsome kind o' goo to settle;
Sic wersh apothecary's broos wi'
As Scotsmen scorn to fyle their moo's wi'.

An', man, I was a blithe hame-comer
Whan first I syndit out my rummer.
Ye should hae seen me then, wi' care
The less important pairts prepare;
Syne, weel contentit wi' it a',
Pour in the speerits wi' a jaw!

I didnae drink, I didnae speak—
I only snowkit up the reek.
I was sae pleased therein to paidle,
I sat an' plowtered wi' my ladle.

An' blithe was I, the morrow's morn,
To daunder through the stookit corn,
And after a' my strange mishanters,
Sit doun amang my ain dissenters.
An', man, it was a joy to me
The pu'pit an' the pews to see,
The pennies dirlin' in the plate,
The elders lookin' on in state;
An' 'mang the first, as it befell,
Wha should I see, sir, but yoursel'?

I was, and I will no deny it,
At the first gliff a hantle tryit
To see yoursel' in sic a station—
It seemed a doubtfü' dispensation.
The feeiin' was a mere digression;
For shüne I understood the session,
An' mindin Aiken an' M'Neil,
I wondered they had düne sae weel.
I saw I had mysel' to blame;
For had I but remained at hame,
Aiblins—though no ava' deservin' 't—
They micht hae named your humble servant.

The kirk was filled, the door was steeked;
Up to the pu'pit ance I keeked;
I was mair pleased than I can tell—
It was the minister himsel'!
Proud, proud was I to see his face,
After sae lang awa' frae grace.
Pleased as I was, I'm no denyin'
Some maitters were not edifyin';
For first I fand—an' here was news!—
Mere hymn-books cockin' in the pews—
A humanized abomination,
Unfit for ony congregation.
Syne, while I still was on the tenter,
I scunnered at the new prezentor;
I thocht him gesterin' an' cauld—
A sair declension frae the auld.
Syne, as though a' the faith was wreckit,
The prayer was not what I'd exspeckit.
Himsel', as it appeared to me,
Was no the man he üsed to be.
But just as I was growin' vext
He waled a maist judeecious text,
An' launchin' into his prelections,
Swoopt, wi' a skirl, on a' defections.

O what a gale was on my speerit
To hear the p'ints o' doctrine clearit,
And a' the horrors o' damnation
Set furth wi' faithfü' ministration!

Nae shauchlin' testimony here—
We were a' damned, an' that was clear.
I owned, wi' gratitude an' wonder,
He was a pleisure to sit under.

XIII

LATE in the nicht in bed I lay,
The winds were at their weary play,
An' tirlin' wa's an' skirlin' wae
    Through heev'n they battered;—
On-ding o' hail, on-blaff o' spray,
    The tempest blattered.

The masoned house it dinled through;
It dung the ship, it cowped the coo';
The rankit aiks it overthrew,
    Had braved a' weathers;
The strang sea-gleds it took an' blew
    Awa' like feathers.

The thraes o' fear on a' were shed,
An' the hair rose, an' slumber fled,
An' lichts were lit an' prayers were said
    Through a' the kintry;
An' the cauld terror clum in bed
    Wi' a' an' sindry.

To hear in the pit-mirk on hie
The brangled collieshangie flie,
The warl' they thocht, wi' land an' sea,
    Itsel' wad cowpit;
An' for auld airn, the smashed debris
    By God be rowpit.

Meanwhile frae far Aldeboran,
To folks wi' talescopes in han',
O' ships that cowpit, winds that ran,
    Nae sign was seen,
But the wee warl' in sunshine span
    As bricht's a preen.

I, tae, by God's especial grace,
Dwall denty in a bieldy place,
Wi' hosened feet, wi' shaven face,
    Wi' dacent mainners:
A grand example to the race
    O' tautit sinners!

The wind may blaw, the heathen rage,
The deil may start on the rampage;—
The sick in bed, the thief in cage—
    What's a' to me?
Cosh in my house, a sober sage,
    I sit an' see.

An' whiles the bluid spangs to my bree,
To lie sae saft, to live sae free,

While better men maun do an' die
      In unco places.
"*Whaur's God?*" I cry, an' "*Whae is me*
      To hae sic graces?"

I mind the fecht the sailors keep,
But fire or can'le, rest or sleep,
In darkness an' the muckle deep;
      An' mind beside
The herd that on the hills o' sheep
      Has wandered wide.

I mind me on the hoastin' weans—
The penny joes on causey stanes—
The auld folk wi' the crazy banes,
      Baith auld an' puir,
That aye maun thole the winds an' rains
      An' labor sair.

An' whiles I'm kind o' pleased a blink,
An' kind o' fleyed forby, to think,
For a' my rowth o' meat an' drink
      An' waste o' crumb,
I'll mebbe have to thole wi' skink
      In Kingdom Come.

For God whan jowes the Judgment bell,
Wi' His ain Hand, His Leevin' Sel',

Sall ryve the guid (as Prophets tell)
  Frae them that had it;
And in the reamin' pat o' hell,
  The rich be scaddit.

O Lord, if this indeed be sae,
Let daw that sair an' happy day!
Again' the warl, grawn auld an' gray,
  Up wi' your aixe!
An' let the puir enjoy their play—
  I'll thole my paiks.

———

XIV

MY CONSCIENCE!

OF a' the ills that flesh can fear,
The loss o' frien's, the lack o' gear,
A yowlin' tyke, a glandered mear,
  A lassie's nonsense—
There's just ae thing I cannae bear,
  An' that's my conscience.

Whan day (an' a' excüse) has gane,
An' wark is düne, an' duty's plain,
An' to my chalmer a' my lane
  I creep apairt,
My conscience! hoo the yammerin' pain
  Stends to my heart!

A' day wi' various ends in view
The hairsts o' time I had to pu',
An' made a hash wad staw a soo,
    Let be a man!—
My conscience! whan my han's were fü',
    Whaur were ye than?

An' there were a' the lures o' life,
There pleesure skirlin' on the fife,
There anger, wi' the hotchin' knife
    Ground shairp in hell—
My conscience!—you that's like a wife!—
    Whaur was yoursel'?

I ken it fine: just waitin' here,
To gar the evil waur appear,
To clart the guid, confüse the clear,
    Mis-ca' the great,
My conscience! an' to raise a steer
    Whan a's ower late.

Sic-like, some tyke grawn auld and blind,
Whan thieves brok' through the gear to
    p'ind,
Has lain his dozened length an' grinned
    At the disaster;
An' the morn's mornin', wud's the wind,
    Yokes on his master.

XV

TO DOCTOR JOHN BROWN

(Whan the dear doctor, dear to a',
Was still amang us here belaw,
I seb my pipes his praise to blaw
Wi' a' my speerit;
But noo, Dear Doctor, he's awa',
An' ne'er can hear it.)

By Lyne and Tyne, by Thames and Tees,
By a' the various river-Dee's,
In Mars and Manors 'yont the seas
          Or here at hame,
Whaure'er there's kindly folk to please,
          They ken your name.

They ken your name, they ken your tyke,
They ken the honey from your byke;
But mebbe after a' your fyke,
          (The trüth to tell)
It' just your honest Rab they like,
          An' no yoursel'.

As at the gowff, some canny play'r
Should tee a common ba' wi' care—
Should flourish and deleever fair
          His souple shintie—
An' the ba' rise into the air,
          A leevin' lintie:

Sae in the game we writers play,
There comes to some a bonny day,
When a dear ferlie shall repay
   Their years o' strife,
An' like your Rab, their things o' clay,
   Spreid wings o' life.

Ye scarce deserved it, I'm afraid—
You that had never learned the trade,
But just some idle mornin' strayed
   Into the schüle,
An' picked the fiddle up an' played
   Like Neil himsel'.

Your e'e was gleg, your fingers dink;
Ye didna fash yoursel' to think,
But wove, as fast as puss can link,
   Your denty wab:—
Ye stapped your pen into the ink,
   An' there was Rab!

Sinsyne, whaure'er your fortune lay
By dowie den, by canty brae,
Simmer an' winter, nicht an' day,
   Rab was aye wi' ye;
An' a' the folk on a' the way
   Were blithe to see ye.

O sir, the gods are kind indeed,
An' hauld ye for an honored heid,

That for a wee bit clarkit screed
      Sae weel reward ye,
An' lend—puir Rabbie bein' deid—
      His ghaist to guard ye.

For though, whaure'er yoursel' may be,
We've just to turn an' glisk a wee,
An' Rab at heel we're shüre to see
      Wi' gladsome caper:—
The bogle of a bogle, he—
      A ghaist o' paper!

And as the auld farrand hero sees
In hell a bogle Hercules,
Pit there the lesser deid to please,
      While he himsel'
Dwalls wi' the muckle gods at ease
      Far raised frae hell:

Sae the true Rabbie far has gane
On kindlier business o' his ain
Wi' aulder frien's; an' his breist-bane
      An' stumpie tailie,
He birstles at a new hearth stane
      By James and Ailie.

XVI

It's an owercome sooth for age an' youth
  And it brooks wi' nae denial,
That the dearest friends are the auldest friends
  And the young are just on trial.

There's a rival bauld wi' young an' auld
  And it's him that has bereft me;
For the sürest friends are the auldest friends
  And the maist o' mine hae left me.

There are kind hearts still, for friends to fill
  And fools to take and break them;
But the nearest friends are the auldest friends
  And the grave's the place to seek them.

A CHILD'S GARDEN OF VERSES

TO ALISON CUNNINGHAM

(FROM HER BOY)

For the long nights you lay awake
And watched for my unworthy sake:
For your most comfortable hand
That led me through the uneven land:
For all the story-books you read:
For all the pains you comforted:
For all you pitied, all you bore,
In sad and happy days of yore:—
My second Mother, my first Wife,
The angel of my infant life—
From the sick child, now well and old
Take, nurse, the little book you hold!

And grant it, Heaven, that all who read
May find as dear a nurse at need,
And every child who lists my rhyme,
In the bright, fireside, nursery clime,
May hear it in as kind a voice
As made my childish days rejoice!

R. L. S.

I

BED IN SUMMER

In winter I get up at night
And dress by yellow candle-light.
In summer, quite the other way,
I have to go to bed by day.

I have to go to bed and see
The birds still hopping on the tree,
Or hear the grown-up people's feet
Still going past me in the street.

And does it not seem hard to you,
When all the sky is clear and blue,
And I should like so much to play,
To have to go to bed by day?

———

II

A THOUGHT

It is very nice to think
The world is full of meat and drink,
With little children saying grace
In every Christian kind of place.

III

AT THE SEASIDE

WHEN I was down beside the sea
A wooden spade they gave to me
  To dig the sandy shore.
My holes were empty like a cup,
In every hole the sea came up,
  Till it could come no more.

———

IV

YOUNG NIGHT THOUGHT

ALL night long and every night,
When my mamma puts out the light,
I see the people marching by,
As plain as day, before my eye.

Armies and emperors and kings,
All carrying different kinds of things,
And marching in so grand a way,
You never saw the like by day.

So fine a show was never seen,
At the great circus on the green;
For every kind of beast and man
Is marching in that caravan.

At first they move a little slow,
But still the faster on they go,
And still beside them close I keep
Until we reach the town of Sleep.

———

V

WHOLE DUTY OF CHILDREN

A CHILD should always say what's true
And speak when he is spoken to,
And behave mannerly at table:
At least as far as he is able.

———

VI

RAIN

THE rain is raining all around,
It falls on field and tree,
It rains on the umbrellas here,
And on the ships at sea.

VII

PIRATE STORY

THREE of us afloat in the meadow by the swing,
    Three of us aboard in the basket on the lea.
Winds are in the air, they are blowing in the
    spring,
    And waves are on the meadow like the waves
    there are at sea.

Where shall we adventure, to-day that we're afloat,
    Wary of the weather and steering by a star?
Shall it be to Africa, a-steering of the boat,
    To Providence, or Babylon, or off to Malabar?

Hi! but here's a squadron a-rowing on the sea—
    Cattle on the meadow a-charging with a roar!
Quick, and we'll escape them, they're as mad as
    they can be,
The wicket is the harbor and the garden is the
    shore.

———

VIII

FOREIGN LANDS

Up into the cherry tree
Who should climb but little me?
I held the trunk with both my hands
And looked abroad on foreign lands.

I saw the next door garden lie,
Adorned with flowers before my eye,
And many pleasant places more
That I had never seen before.

I saw the dimpling river pass
And be the sky's blue looking-glass;
The dusty roads go up and down
With people tramping into town.

If I could find a higher tree
Further and further I should see,
To where the grown up river slips
Into the sea among the ships,

To where the roads on either hand
Lead onward into fairy land,
Where all the children dine at five,
And all the playthings come alive.

IX

WINDY NIGHTS

WHENEVER the moon and stars are set,
  Whenever the wind is high,
All night long in the dark and wet,
  A man goes riding by.
Late in the night when the fires are
      out,
Why does he gallop and gallop about?

Whenever the trees are crying aloud,
  And ships are tossed at sea,
By, on the highway, low and loud,
  By at the gallop goes he.
By at the gallop he goes, and then
By he comes back at the gallop again.

———

X

TRAVEL

I SHOULD like to rise and go
Where the golden apples grow;—
Where below another sky
Parrot islands anchored lie,

And,   watched by cockatoos and
    goats,
Lonely Crusoes building boats;—
Where in sunshine reaching out
Eastern cities, miles about,
Are with mosque and minaret
Among sandy gardens set,
And the rich goods from near
    and far
Hang for sale in the bazaar;—
Where the Great Wall round China
    goes,
And on one side the desert blows,
And with bell and voice and drum,
Cities on the other hum;—
Where are forests, hot as fire,
Wide as England, tall as a spire,
Full of apes and cocoa-nuts
And the negro hunters' huts;—
Where the knotty crocodile
Lies and blinks in the Nile,
And the red flamingo flies
Hunting fish before his eyes;—
Where in jungles, near and far,
Man-devouring tigers are,
Lying close and giving ear
Lest the hunt be drawing near,
Or a comer-by be seen

Swinging in a palanquin;—
Where among the desert sands
Some deserted city stands,
All its children, sweep and prince
Grown to manhood ages since,
Not a foot in street or house,
Not a stir of child or mouse,
And when kindly falls the night,
In all the town no spark of light.
There I'll come when I'm a man
With a camel caravan;
Light a fire in the gloom
Of some dusty dining-room;
See the pictures on the walls,
Heroes, fights and festivals;
And in a corner find the toys
Of the old Egyptian boys.

———

XI

SINGING

OF speckled eggs the birdie sings
And nests among the trees;
The sailor sings of ropes and things
In ships upon the seas.

The children sing in far Japan,
  The children sing in Spain;
The organ with the organ man
  Is singing in the rain.

———

XII

LOOKING FORWARD

WHEN I am grown to man's estate
I shall be very proud and great,
And tell the other girls and boys
Not to meddle with my toys.

———

XIII

A GOOD PLAY

WE built a ship upon the stairs
All made of the back-bedroom chairs,
And filled it full of sofa pillows
To go a-sailing on the billows.

We took a saw and several nails,
And water in the nursery pails;
And Tom said, "Let us also take
An apple and a slice of cake;"—

Which was enough for Tom and me
To go a-sailing on, till tea.

We sailed along for days and days
And had the very best of plays;
But Tom fell out and hurt his knee
So there was no one left but me.

———

XIV

WHERE GO THE BOATS?

Dark brown is the river,
 Golden is the sand.
It flows along forever,
 With trees on either hand.

Green leaves a-floating,
 Castles of the foam,
Boats of mine a-boating—
 Where will all come home?

On goes the river
 And out past the mill,
Away down the valley,
 Away down the hill.

Away down the river,
A hundred miles or more,
Other little children
Shall bring my boats ashore.

———

XV

AUNTIE'S SKIRTS

WHENEVER Auntie moves around,
Her dresses make a curious sound;
They trail behind her up the floor,
And trundle after through the door.

———

XVI

THE LAND OF COUNTERPANE

WHEN I was sick and lay a-bed,
I had two pillows at my head,
And all my toys beside me lay
To keep me happy all the day.

And sometimes for an hour or so
I watched my leaden soldiers go,

With different uniforms and drills,
Among the bed-clothes through the
    hills;

And sometimes sent my ships in fleets
All up and down among the sheets;
Or brought my trees and houses out,
And planted cities all about.

I was the giant great and still
That sits upon the pillow-hill,
And sees before him, dale and plain,
The pleasant land of counterpane.

––––––

XVII

THE LAND OF NOD

FROM breakfast on through all the
    day
At home among my friends I stay;
But every night I go abroad
Afar into the land of Nod.

All by myself I have to go,
With none to tell me what to do—
All alone beside the streams
And up the mountain-sides of dreams.

The strangest things are there for me,
Both things to eat and things to see
And many frightening sights abroad
Till morning in the land of Nod.

Try as I like to find the way,
I never can get back by day,
Nor can remember plain and clear
The curious music that I hear.

XVIII

MY SHADOW

I HAVE a little shadow that goes in and out with
  me,
And what can be the use of him is more than I
  can see.
He is very, very like me from the heels up to
  the head;
And I see him jump before me, when I jump
  into my bed.

The funniest thing about him is the way he likes
  to grow—
Not at all like proper children, which is always
  very slow;

For he sometimes shoots up taller like an india
    rubber ball,
And he sometimes gets so little that there's none
    of him at all.

He hasn't got a notion of how children ought to
    play,
And can only make a fool of me in every sort
    of way.

He stays so close beside me, he's a coward you
    can see;
I'd think shame to stick to nursie as that shadow
    sticks to me!

One morning, very early, before the sun was up,
I rose and found the shining dew on every
    buttercup;
But my lazy little shadow, like an arrant sleepy-
    head,
Had stayed at home behind me and was fast
    asleep in bed.

————

XIX

SYSTEM

EVERY night my prayers I say,
And get my dinner every day;
And every day that I've been good,
I get an orange after food.

The child that is not clean and neat,
With lots of toys and things to eat,
He is a naughty child, I'm sure—
Or else his dear papa is poor.

———

XX

A GOOD BOY

I woke before the morning, I was happy all the
    day,
I never said an ugly word, but smiled and stuck
    to play.

And now at last the sun is going down behind
    the wood,
And I am very happy, for I know that I've been
    good.

My bed is waiting cool and fresh, with linen
    smooth and fair,
And I must off to sleepsin-by, and not forget
    my prayer.

I know that, till to-morrow I shall see the sun
    arise,
No ugly dream shall fright my mind, no ugly
    sight my eyes,

But slumber hold me tightly till I waken in the
    dawn,
And hear the thrushes singing in the lilacs
    round the lawn.

XXI

ESCAPE AT BEDTIME

THE lights from the parlor and kitchen shone out
    Through the blinds and the windows and bars;
And high overhead and all moving about,
    There were thousands of millions of stars.
There ne'er were such thousands of leaves on a
    tree,
    Nor of people in church or the Park,
As the crowds of the stars that looked down
    upon me,
    And that glittered and winked in the dark.

The Dog, and the Plow, and the Hunter, and all,
    And the star of the sailor, and Mars,
These shone in the sky, and the pail by the wall
    Would be half full of water and stars.
They saw me at last, and they chased me with
    cries,
    And they soon had me packed into bed;

But the glory kept shining and bright in my
    eyes,
And the stars going round in my head.

———

XXII

MARCHING SONG

Bring the comb and play upon it!
  Marching, here we come!
Willie cocks his highland bonnet,
  Johnnie beats the drum.

Mary Jane commands the party,
  Peter leads the rear;
Feet in time, alert and hearty,
  Each a Grenadier!

All in the most martial manner
  Marching double-quick;
While the napkin like a banner
  Waves upon the stick!

Here's enough of fame and pillage,
  Great commander Jane!
Now that we've been round the village,
  Let's go home again.

XXIII

THE COW

THE friendly cow all red and white,
    I love with all my heart:
She gives me cream with all her might,
    To eat with apple-tart.

She wanders lowing here and there,
    And yet she cannot stray,
All in the pleasant open air,
    The pleasant light of day;

And blown by all the winds that pass
    And wet with all the showers,
She walks among the meadow grass
    And eats the meadow flowers.

XXIV

HAPPY THOUGHT

THE world is so full of a number of things,
I'm sure we should all be as happy as kings.

XXV

THE WIND

I saw you toss the kites on high
And blow the birds about the sky;
And all around I heard you pass,
Like ladies' skirts across the grass—
     O wind, a-blowing all day long,
     O wind, that sings so loud a song!

I saw the different things you did,
But always you yourself you hid,
I felt you push, I heard you call,
I could not see yourself at all—
     O wind, a-blowing all day long,
     O wind, that sings so loud a song!

O you that are so strong and cold,
O blower, are you young or old?
Are you a beast of field and tree,
Or just a stronger child than me?
     O wind, a-blowing all day long,
     O wind, that sings so loud a song!

XXVI

KEEPSAKE MILL

OVER the borders, a sin without pardon,
  Breaking the branches and crawling below,
Out through the breach in the wall of the
    garden,
  Down by the banks of the river, we go.

Here is the mill with the humming of thunder,
  Here is the weir with the wonder of foam,
Here is the sluice with the race running
    under—
  Marvelous places, though handy to home!

Sounds of the village grow stiller and stiller,
  Stiller the notes of the birds on the hill;
Dusty and dim are the eyes of the miller,
  Deaf are his ears with the moil of the mill.

Years may go by, and the wheel in the river
  Wheels as it wheels for us, children, to-day,
Wheel and keep roaring and foaming forever
  Long after all of the boys are away.

Home from the Indies and home from the ocean,
  Heroes and soldiers we all shall come home;
Still we shall find the old mill-wheel in motion,
  Turning and churning that river to foam.

You with the bean that I gave when we quar-
  reled,
I with your marble of Saturday last,
Honored and old and all gayly appareled,
  Here we shall meet and remember the past.

———

XXVII

GOOD AND BAD CHILDREN

CHILDREN, you are very little,
And your bones are very brittle;
If you would grow great and stately,
You must try to walk sedately.

You must still be bright and quiet,
And content with simple diet;
And remain through all bewild'ring,
Innocent and honest children.

Happy hearts and happy faces,
Happy play in grassy places—
That was how in ancient ages,
Children grew to kings and sages.

But the unkind and the unruly,
And the sort who eat unduly,
They must never hope for glory—
Theirs is quite a different story!

Cruel children, crying babies,
All grow up as geese and gabies,
Hated, as their age increases,
By their nephews and their nieces.

————

XXVIII

FOREIGN CHILDREN

LITTLE Indian, Sioux or Crow,
Little frosty Eskimo,
Little Turk or Japanee,
O! don't you wish that you were
    me?

You have seen the scarlet trees
And the lions over seas;
You have eaten ostrich eggs,
And turned the turtles off their
    legs.

Such a life is very fine,
But it's not so nice as mine:
You must often, as you trod,
Have wearied *not* to be abroad.

You have curious things to eat,
I am fed on proper meat;

You must dwell beyond the foam,
But I am safe and live at home.

Little Indian, Sioux or Crow,
Little frosty Eskimo,
Little Turk or Japanee,
O! don't you wish that you were
    me?

———

XXIX

THE SUN'S TRAVELS

THE sun is not a-bed, when I
At night upon my pillow lie;
Still round the earth his way he takes,
And morning after morning makes.

While here at home, in shining day,
We round the sunny garden play,
Each little Indian sleepy-head
Is being kissed and put to bed.

And when at eve I rise from tea,
Day dawns beyond the Atlantic Sea,
And all the children in the West
Are getting up and being dressed.

XXX

THE LAMPLIGHTER

My tea is nearly ready and the sun has left the
    sky;
It's time to take the window to see Leerie going
    by;
For every night at teatime and before you take
    your seat,
With lantern and with ladder he comes posting
    up the street.

Now Tom would be a driver and Maria go to
    sea,
And my papa's a banker and as rich as he can
    be;
But I, when I am stronger and can choose what
    I'm to do,
O Leerie, I'll go round at night and light the
    lamps with you.

For we are very lucky, with a lamp before the
    door,
And Leerie stops to light it as he lights so many
    more;
And O! before you hurry by with ladder and
    with light,
O Leerie, see a little child and nod to him to-
    night!

XXXI

MY BED IS A BOAT

My bed is like a little boat;
  Nurse helps me in when I em-
    bark;
She girds me in my sailor's coat
  And starts me in the dark.

At night I go on board and say
  Good-night to all my friends on
    shore;
I shut my eyes and sail away
  And see and hear no more.

And sometimes things to bed I take,
  As prudent sailors have to do:
Perhaps a slice of wedding-cake,
  Perhaps a toy or two.

All night across the dark we steer:
  But when the day returns at last,
Safe in my room beside the pier,
  I find my vessel fast.

———

XXXII

THE MOON

THE moon has a face like the clock in the
    hall;
She shines on thieves on the garden wall,
On streets and fields and harbor quays,
And birdies asleep in the forks of the trees.

The squalling cat and the squeaking mouse,
The howling dog by the door of the house,
The bat that lies in bed at noon,
All love to be out by the light of the moon.

But all of the things that belong to the day
Cuddle to sleep to be out of her way;
And flowers and children close their eyes
Till up in the morning the sun shall arise.

———

XXXIII

THE SWING

How do you like to go up in a
    swing,
  Up in the air so blue?
Oh, I do think it the pleasantest
    thing
  Ever a child can do!

Up in the air and over the wall,
  Till I can see so wide,
Rivers and trees and cattle and all
  Over the countryside—

Till I look down on the garden
    green,
  Down on the roof so brown—
Up in the air I go flying again,
  Up in the air and down!

XXXIV

TIME TO RISE

A BIRDIE with a yellow bill
Hopped upon the window-sill,
Cocked his shining eye and said:
"Ain't you 'shamed, you sleepy-head?"

XXXV

LOOKING-GLASS RIVER

SMOOTH it slides upon its travel,
  Here a wimple, there a gleam—
    O the clean gravel!
    O the smooth stream!

Sailing blossoms, silver fishes,
 Paven pools as clear as air—
  How a child wishes
  To live down there!

We can see our colored faces
 Floating on the shaken pool
  Down in cool places,
  Dim and very cool;

Till a wind or water wrinkle,
 Dipping martin, plumping trout,
  Spreads in a twinkle
  And blots all out.

See the rings pursue each other;
 All below grows black as night,
  Just as if mother
  Had blown out the light!

Patience, children, just a minute—
 See the spreading circles die;
  The stream and all in it
  Will clear by-and-by.

XXXVI

FAIRY BREAD

COME up here, O dusty feet!
Here is fairy bread to eat.
Here in my retiring room,
   Children, you may dine
On the golden smell of broom
   And the shade of pine;
And when you have eaten well,
Fairy stories hear and tell.

———

XXXVII

FROM A RAILWAY CARRIAGE

FASTER than fairies, faster than witches,
Bridges and houses, hedges and ditches;
And charging along like troops in a battle,
All through the meadows the horses and cattle:
All of the sights of the hill and the plain
Fly as thick as driving rain;
And ever again in the wink of an eye,
Painted stations whistle by.

Here is a child who clambers and scrambles,
All by himself and gathering brambles;
Here is a tramp who stands and gazes;
And there is the green for stringing the daisies!
Here is a cart run away in the road
Lumping along with man and load;
And here is a mill and there is a river:
Each a glimpse and gone forever!

XXXVIII

WINTER-TIME

Late lies the wintry sun a-bed,
A frosty, fiery sleepy-head;
Blinks but an hour or two; and then,
A blood-red orange, sets again.

Before the stars have left the skies,
At morning in the dark I rise;
And shivering in my nakedness,
By the cold candle, bathe and dress.

Close by the jolly fire I sit
To warm my frozen bones a bit;
Or with a reindeer-sled explore
The colder countries round the door.

When to go out my nurse doth wrap
Me in my comforter and cap:
The cold wind burns my face, and blows
Its frosty pepper up my nose.

Black are my steps on silver sod;
Thick blows my frosty breath abroad;
And tree and house, and hill and lake,
Are frosted like a wedding-cake.

―――

XXXIX

THE HAYLOFT

THROUGH all the pleasant meadow-side
    The grass grew shoulder-high,
Till the shining scythes went far and wide
    And cut it down to dry.

These green and sweetly-smelling crops
    They led in wagons home;
And they piled them here in mountain-tops
    For mountaineers to roam.

Here is Mount Clear, Mount Rusty Nail,
    Mount Eagle and Mount High;―
The mice that in these mountains dwell,
    No happier are than I!

O what a joy to clamber there,
    O what a place for play,
With the sweet, the dim, the dusty air,
    The happy hills of hay.

———

XL

FAREWELL TO THE FARM

The coach is at the door at last;
The eager children mounting fast
And kissing hands, in chorus sing:
Good-by, good-by, to everything!

To house and garden, field and lawn,
The meadow-gates we swung upon,
To pump and stable, tree and swing,
Good-by, good-by, to everything!

And fare you well for evermore,
O ladder at the hayloft door,
O hayloft where the cobwebs cling,
Good-by, good-by, to everything!

Crack goes the whip, and off we go;
The trees and houses smaller grow;
Last, round the woody turn we swing:
Good-by, good-by, to everything!

XLI

NORTH–WEST PASSAGE

1. GOOD-NIGHT

WHEN the bright lamp is carried in,
The sunless hours again begin;
O'er all without, in field and lane,
The haunted night returns again.

Now we behold the embers flee
About the firelit hearth; and see
Our faces painted as we pass,
Like pictures, on the window-glass.

Must we to bed indeed? Well then,
Let us arise and go like men,
And face with an undaunted tread
The long black passage up to bed.

Farewell, O brother, sister, sire!
O pleasant party round the fire!
The songs you sing, the tales you tell,
Till far to-morrow, fare ye well!

———

2. SHADOW MARCH

All round the house is the jet-black night;
  It stares through the window-pane;
It crawls in the corners, hiding from the light,
  And it moves with the moving flame.

Now my little heart goes a-beating like a drum,
  With the breath of the Bogie in my hair;
And all round the candle the crooked shadows come
  And go marching along up the stair.

The shadow of the balusters, the shadow of the lamp,
  The shadow of the child that goes to bed—
All the wicked shadows coming, tramp, tramp, tramp,
  With the black night overhead.

---

3. IN PORT

Last, to the chamber where I lie
My fearful footsteps patter nigh,
  And come from out the cold and gloom
  Into my warm and cheerful room.

There, safe arrived, we turn about
To keep the coming shadows out,
And close the happy door at last
On all the perils that we past.

Then, when mamma goes by to bed,
She shall come in with tiptoe tread,
And see me lying warm and fast
And in the Land of Nod at last.

THE CHILD ALONE

I

THE UNSEEN PLAYMATE

WHEN children are playing alone on the green,
In comes the playmate that never was seen.
When children are happy and lonely and good,
The Friend of the Children comes out of the
    wood.

Nobody heard him and nobody saw,
His is a picture you never could draw,
But he's sure to be present, abroad or at home,
When children are happy and playing alone.

He lies in the laurels, he runs on the grass,
He sings when you tinkle the musical glass;
Whene'er you are happy and cannot tell why,
The Friend of the Children is sure to be by!

He loves to be little, he hates to be big,
'Tis he that inhabits the caves that you dig;
'Tis he when you play with your soldiers of tin
That sides with the Frenchmen and never can
    win.

'Tis he when at night you go off to your bed,
Bids you go to your sleep and not trouble your
     head;
For wherever they're lying, in cupboard or shelf,
'Tis he will take care of your playthings himself!

II

MY SHIP AND I

O it's I that am the captain of a tidy little ship,
   Of a ship that goes a-sailing on the pond;
And my ship it keeps a-turning all around and
      all about;
But when I'm a little older, I shall find the secret
      out
   How to send my vessel sailing on beyond.

For I mean to grow as little as the dolly at the
      helm,
   And the dolly I intend to come alive;
And with him beside to help me, it's a-sailing I
      shall go,
It's a sailing on the water, when the jolly breezes
      blow
   And the vessel goes a divie-divie-dive.

O it's then you'll see me sailing through the
        rushes and the reeds,
    And you'll hear the water singing at the prow;
For beside the dolly sailor I'm to voyage and
        explore,
To land upon the island where no dolly was be-
        fore,
    And to fire the penny cannon in the bow.

────

III

MY KINGDOM

Down by a shining water well
I found a very little dell,
        No higher than my head.
The heather and the gorse about
In summer bloom were coming out,
        Some yellow and some red.

I called the little pool a sea;
The little hills were big to me;
        For I am very small.
I made a boat, I made a town,
I searched the caverns up and down,
        And named them one and all.

And all about was mine, I said,
The little sparrows overhead,
    The little minnows too.
This was the world and I was king;
For me the bees came by to sing,
    For me the swallows flew.

I played there were no deeper seas,
Nor any wider plains than these,
    Nor other kings than me.
At last I heard my mother call
Out from the house at evenfall,
    To call me home to tea.

And I must rise and leave my dell,
And leave my dimpled water well,
    And leave my heather blooms.
Alas! and as my home I neared
How very big my nurse appeared,
    How great and cool the rooms!

———

IV

PICTURE BOOKS IN WINTER

Summer fading, winter comes—
Frosty mornings, tingling thumbs,
Window robins, winter rooks,
And the picture story-books.

Water now is turned to stone
Nurse and I can walk upon;
Still we find the flowing brooks
In the picture story-books.

All the pretty things put by,
Wait upon the children's eye,
Sheep and shepherds, trees and crooks,
In the picture story-books.

We may see how all things are,
Seas and cities, near and far,
And the flying fairies' looks,
In the picture story-books.

How am I to sing your praise,
Happy chimney-corner days,
Sitting safe in nursery nooks,
Reading picture story-books?

V

MY TREASURES

THESE nuts that I keep in the back of the nest
Where all my lead soldiers are lying at rest,
Were gathered in autumn by nursie and me
In a wood with a well by the side of the sea.

This whistle we made (and how clearly it sounds!)
By the side of a field at the end of the grounds.
Of a branch of a plane, with a knife of my own,
It was nursie who made it, and nursie alone!

The stone, with the white and the yellow and
        gray,
We discovered I cannot tell *how* far away;
And I carried it back, although weary and cold,
For though father denies it, I'm sure it is gold.

But of all of my treasures the last is the king,
For there's very few children possess such a thing;
And that is a chisel, both handle and blade,
Which a man who was really a carpenter made.

———

VI

BLOCK CITY

WHAT are you able to build with your blocks?
Castles and palaces, temples and docks.
Rain may keep raining, and others go roam,
But I can be happy and building at home.

Let the sofa be mountains, the carpet be sea,
There I'll establish a city for me:
A kirk and a mill and a palace beside,
And a harbor as well where my vessels may
    ride.

Great is the palace with pillar and wall,
A sort of a tower on the top of it all,
And steps coming down in an orderly way
To where my toy vessels lie safe in the bay.

This one is sailing and that one is moored:
Hark to the song of the sailors on board!
And see on the steps of my palace the kings
Coming and going with presents and things!

Now I have done with it, down let it go!
All in a moment the town is laid low.
Block upon block lying scattered and free,
What is there left of my town by the sea?

Yet as I saw it, I see it again,
The kirk and the palace, the ships and the men,
And as long as I live and where'er I may be,
I'll always remember my town by the sea.

———

VII

THE LAND OF STORY-BOOKS

At evening when the lamp is lit,
Around the fire my parents sit;
They sit at home and talk and sing,
And do not play at anything.

Now, with my little gun, I crawl
All in the dark along the wall,
And follow round the forest track
Away behind the sofa back.

There, in the night, where none can
    spy,
All in my hunter's camp I lie,
And play at books that I have read
Till it is time to go to bed.

These are the hills, these are the
    woods,
These are my starry solitudes;

And there the river by whose brink
The roaring lions come to drink.

I see the others far away
As if in firelit camp they lay,
And I, like to an Indian scout,
Around their party prowled about.

So, when my nurse comes in for me,
Home I return across the sea,
And go to bed with backward looks
At my dear land of Story-books.

———

VIII

ARMIES IN THE FIRE

The lamps now glitter down the street;
Faintly sound the falling feet;
And the blue even slowly falls
About the garden trees and walls.

Now in the falling of the gloom
The red fire paints the empty room:
And warmly on the roof it looks,
And flickers on the backs of books.

Armies march by tower and spire
Of cities blazing, in the fire;—
Till as I gaze with staring eyes,
The armies fade, the luster dies.

Then once again the glow returns;
Again the phantom city burns;
And down the red-hot valley, lo!
The phantom armies marching go!

Blinking embers, tell me true
Where are those armies marching to,
And what the burning city is
That crumbles in your furnaces!

IX

THE LITTLE LAND

WHEN at home alone I sit
And am very tired of it,
I have just to shut my eyes
To go sailing through the skies—
To go sailing far away
To the pleasant Land of Play;
To the fairy land afar
Where the Little People are;

Where the clover-tops are trees,
And the rain-pools are the seas,
And the leaves like little ships
Sail about on tiny trips;
And above the daisy tree
     Through the grasses,
High o'erhead the Bumble Bee
     Hums and passes.

In that forest to and fro
I can wander, I can go;
See the spider and the fly,
And the ants go marching by
Carrying parcels with their feet
Down the green and grassy street.
I can in the sorrel sit
Where the ladybird alit.
I can climb the jointed grass;
    And on high
See the greater swallows pass
    In the sky,
And the round sun rolling by
Heeding no such things as I.

Through that forest I can pass
Till, as in a looking-glass,
Humming fly and daisy tree
And my tiny self I see,

Painted very clear and neat
On the rain-pool at my feet.
Should a leaflet come to land
Drifting near to where I stand,
Straight I'll board that tiny boat
Round the rain-pool sea to float.

Little thoughtful creatures sit
On the grassy coasts of it;
Little things with lovely eyes
See me sailing with surprise.
Some are clad in armor green—
(These have sure to battle been!)—
Some are pied with ev'ry hue,
Black and crimson, gold and blue;
Some have wings and swift are
     gone;—
But they all look kindly on.

When my eyes I once again
Open, and see all things plain:
High bare walls, great bare floor;
Great big knobs on drawer and
     door;
Great big people perched on chairs,
Stitching tucks and mending tears,
Each a hill that I could climb,
And talking nonsense all the time—

O dear me,
That I could be
A sailor on the rain-pool sea,
A climber in the clover tree,
And just come back, a sleepy-head,
Late at night to go to bed.

GARDEN DAYS

——

I

NIGHT AND DAY

WHEN the golden day is done,
  Through the closing portal,
Child and garden, flower and sun,
  Vanish all things mortal.

As the blinding shadows fall,
  As the rays diminish,
Under evening's cloak, they all
  Roll away and vanish.

Garden darkened, daisy shut,
  Child in bed, they slumber—
Glow-worm in the highway rut,
  Mice among the lumber.

In the darkness houses shine,
  Parents move with candles;
Till on all the night divine
  Turns the bedroom handles.

Till at last the day begins
  In the east a-breaking,
In the hedges and the whins
  Sleeping birds a-waking.

In the darkness shapes of things,
  Houses, trees, and hedges,
Clearer grow; and sparrow's wings
  Beat on window ledges.

These shall wake the yawning maid;
  She the door shall open—
Finding dew on garden glade
  And the morning broken.

There my garden grows again
  Green and rosy painted,
As at eve behind the pane
  From my eyes it fainted.

Just as it was shut away,
  Toy-like in the even,
Here I see it glow with day
  Under glowing heaven.

Every path and every plot,
  Every bush of roses,
Every blue forget-me-not
  Where the dew reposes,

"Up!" they cry, "the day is come
  On the smiling valleys:
We have beat the morning drum;
  Playmate, join your allies!"

———

II

NEST EGGS

Birds all the sunny day
  Flutter and quarrel
Here in the arbor-like
  Tent of the laurel.

Here in the fork
  The brown nest is seated;
Four little blue eggs
  The mother keeps heated.

While we stand watching her,
  Staring like gabies,
Safe in each egg are the
  Bird's little babies.

Soon the frail eggs they shall
  Chip, and upspringing
Make all the April woods
  Merry with singing.

Younger than we are,
    O children, and frailer,
Soon in blue air they'll be,
    Singer and sailor.

We so much older,
    Taller and stronger,
We shall look down on the
    Birdies no longer.

They shall go flying
    With musical speeches
High overhead in the
    Tops of the beeches.

In spite of our wisdom
    And sensible talking,
We on our feet must go
    Plodding and walking.

———

III

THE FLOWERS

ALL the names I know from nurse:
Gardener's garters, Shepherd's purse,
Bachelor's buttons, Lady's smock,
And the Lady Hollyhock.

Fairy places, fairy things,
Fairy woods where the wild bee wings,
Tiny trees for tiny dames—
These must all be fairy names!

Tiny woods below whose boughs
Shady fairies weave a house;
Tiny tree-tops, rose or thyme,
Where the braver fairies climb!

Fair are grown-up people's trees,
But the fairest woods are these;
Where if I were not so tall,
I should live for good and all.

IV

SUMMER SUN

GREAT is the sun, and wide he goes
Through empty heaven without repose;
And in the blue and glowing days
More thick than rain he showers his rays.

Though closer still the blinds we pull
To keep the shady parlor cool,
Yet he will find a chink or two
To slip his golden fingers through.

The dusty attic, spider-clad,
He through the key-hole maketh glad;
And through the broken edge of tiles,
Into the laddered hayloft smiles.

Meantime his golden face around
He bares to all the garden ground,
And sheds a warm and glittering look
Among the ivy's inmost nook.

Above the hills, along the blue,
·Round the bright air with footing true,
To please the child, to paint the rose,
The gardener of the World, he goes.

———

V

THE DUMB SOLDIER

When the grass was closely mown,
Walking on the lawn alone,
In the turf a hole I found
And hid a soldier underground.

Spring and daisies came apace;
Grasses hide my hiding-place;
Grasses run like a green sea
O'er the lawn up to my knee.

Under grass alone he lies,
Looking up with leaden eyes,
Scarlet coat and pointed gun,
To the stars and to the sun.

When the grass is ripe like grain,
When the scythe is stoned again,
When the lawn is shaven clear,
Then my hole shall reappear.

I shall find him, never fear,
I shall find my grenadier;
But for all that's gone and come,
I shall find my soldier dumb.

He has lived, a little thing,
In the grassy woods of spring;
Done, if he could tell me true
Just as I should like to do.

He has seen the starry hours
And the springing of the flowers;
And the fairy things that pass
In the forests of the grass.

In the silence he has heard
Talking bee and ladybird,
And the butterfly has flown,
O'er him as he lay alone.

Not a word will he disclose,
Not a word of all he knows.
I must lay him on the shelf,
And make up the tale myself.

———

VI

AUTUMN FIRES

In the other gardens
    And all up the vale,
From the autumn bonfires
    See the smoke trail!

Pleasant summer over
    And all the summer flowers,
The red fire blazes,
    The gray smoke towers.

Sing a song of seasons!
    Something bright in all!
Flowers in the summer,
    Fires in the fall!

———

VII

THE GARDENER

THE gardener does not love to talk,
He makes me keep the gravel walk;
And when he puts his tools away,
He locks the door and takes the key.

Away behind the currant row
Where no one else but cook may go,
Far in the plots, I see him dig,
Old and serious, brown and big.

He digs the flowers, green, red, and
      blue,
Nor wishes to be spoken to.
He digs the flowers and cuts the hay,
And never seems to want to play.

Silly gardener! summer goes,
And winter comes with pinching toes,
When in the garden bare and brown
You must lay your barrow down.

Well now, and while the summer stays,
To profit by these garden days,
O how much wiser you would be
To play at Indian wars with me!

VIII

HISTORICAL ASSOCIATIONS

DEAR Uncle Jim, this garden ground
That now you smoke your pipe around,
Has seen immortal actions done
And valiant battles lost and won.

Here we had best on tip-toe tread,
While I for safety march ahead,
For this is that enchanted ground
Where all who loiter slumber sound.

Here is the sea, here is the sand,
Here is simple Shepherd's Land,
Here are the fairy hollyhocks,
And there are Ali Baba's rocks.

But yonder, see! apart and high,
Frozen Siberia lies; where I,
With Robert Bruce and William Tell,
Was bound by an enchanter's spell.

There, then, awhile in chains we lay,
In wintry dungeons, far from day;
But ris'n at length, with might and main,
Our iron fetters burst in twain.

Then all the horns were blown in town;
And to the ramparts clanging down,
All the giants leaped to horse
And charged behind us through the
          gorse.

On we rode, the others and I,
Over the mountains blue, and by
The Silver River, the sounding sea,
And the robber woods of Tartary.

A thousand miles we galloped fast,
And down the witches' lane we passed,
And rode amain, with brandished sword,
Up to the middle, through the ford.

Last we drew rein—a weary three—
Upon the lawn, in time for tea,
And from our steeds alighted down
Before the gates of Babylon.

ENVOYS

I

TO WILLIE AND HENRIETTA

If two may read aright
These rhymes of old delight
And house and garden play,
You two, my cousins, and you only, may.

You in a garden green
With me were king and queen,
Were hunter, soldier, tar,
And all the thousand things that children are.

Now in the elders' seat
We rest with quiet feet,
And from the window-bay
We watch the children, our successors, play.

"Time was," the golden head
Irrevocably said;
But time which none can bind,
While flowing fast away, leaves love behind.

II

TO MY MOTHER

You too, my mother, read my rhymes
For love of unforgotten times,
And you may chance to hear once more
The little feet along the floor.

———

III

TO AUNTIE

Chief of our aunts—not only I,
But all your dozen of nurslings cry—
What did the other children do?
And what were childhood, wanting you?

———

IV

TO MINNIE

THE red room with the giant bed
Where none but elders laid their head;

The little room where you and I
Did for a while together lie
And, simple suitor, I your hand
In decent marriage did demand;
The great day nursery, best of all,
With pictures pasted on the wall
And leaves upon the blind—
A pleasant room wherein to wake
And hear the leafy garden shake
And rustle in the wind—
And pleasant there to lie in bed
And see the pictures overhead—
The wars about Sebastopol,
The grinning guns along the wall,
The daring escalade,
The plunging ships, the bleating sheep,
The happy children ankle-deep
And laughing as they wade:
All these are vanished clean away,
And the old manse is changed to-day;
It wears an altered face
And shields a stranger race.
The river, on from mill to mill,
Flows past our childhood's garden still;
But ah! we children nevermore
Shall watch it from the water-door!
Below the yew—it still is there—
Our phantom voices haunt the air

As we were still at play,
And I can hear them call and say:
"How far is it to Babylon?"

Ah, far enough, my dear,
Far, far enough from here—
Yet you have further gone!
"Can I get there by candle-light?"
So goes the old refrain.
I do not know—perchance you might—
But only, children, hear it right,
Ah, never to return again!
The eternal dawn, beyond a doubt,
Shall break on hill and plain,
And put all stars and candles out,
Ere we be young again.

To you in distant India, these
I send across the seas,
Nor count it far across.
For which of us forgets
The Indian cabinets,
The bones of antelope, the wings of albatross,
The pied and painted birds and beans,
The junks and bangles, beads and screens,
The gods and sacred bells,
And the loud-humming, twisted shells?
The level of the parlor floor
Was honest, homely, Scottish shore;

But when we climbed upon a chair,
Behold the gorgeous East was there!
Be this a fable; and behold
Me in the parlor as of old,
And Minnie just above me set
In the quaint Indian cabinet!
Smiling and kind, you grace a shelf
Too high for me to reach myself.
Reach down a hand, my dear, and take
These rhymes for old acquaintance' sake.

———

V

TO MY NAME-CHILD

1

SOME day soon this rhyming volume, if you learn
    with proper speed,
Little Louis Sanchez, will be given you to read.
Then shall you discover, that your name was
    printed down
By the English printers, long before, in London
    town.

In the great and busy city where the East and
    West are met,
All the little letters did the English printer set;
While you thought of nothing, and were still too
    young to play,
Foreign people thought of you in places far away.

Ay, and while you slept, a baby, over all the
    English lands
Other little children took the volume in their
    hands;
Other children questioned, in their homes across
    the seas:
Who was little Louis, won't you tell us, mother,
    please?

2

Now that you have spelt your lesson, lay it down
    and go and play,
Seeking shells and seaweed on the sands of
    Monterey,
Watching all the mighty whalebones, lying buried
    by the breeze,
Tiny sandy-pipers, and the huge Pacific seas.

And remember in your playing, as the sea-fog
    rolls to you,
Long ere you could read it, how I told you what
    to do;

And that while you thought of no one, nearly
      half the world away
Some one thought of Louis on the beach of
      Monterey!

———

VI

TO ANY READER

As from the house your mother sees
You playing round the garden trees,
So you may see, if you will look
Through the windows of this book,
Another child, far, far away,
And in another garden, play.
But do not think you can at all,
By knocking on the window, call
That child to hear you. He intent
Is all on his play-business bent.
He does not hear; he will not look,
Nor yet be lured out of this book.
For, long ago, the truth to say,
He has grown up and gone away,
And it is but a child of air
That lingers in the garden there.

END OF VOLUME FIFTEEN.